Oral Embryology
and
Microscopic Anatomy

FIGURE 1.—A photomicrograph of a ground section cut faciolingually through a human maxillary first premolar tooth. The enamel has a deep fissure in the central developmental groove. At the entrance to the fissure, on the triangular ridge of the buccal cusp, there is a barely visible dark area which is probably the beginning of a carious lesion. There is no evidence of caries at the bottom of the fissure.

In the enamel on the buccal and on the lingual surfaces of the crown there may be faintly seen near the dentinoenamel junction the narrow light and dark areas which are the bands of Hunter-Schreger.

Notice the curvature of the dentinal tubules in the crown of the tooth. Notice the configuration of the pulp chamber: the pulp horn in the buccal cusp extends much farther occlusally than the pulp horn in the lingual cusp. The pulp cavity here is empty because the pulp tissue was destroyed in the preparation of the section. Notice the relatively narrow root canals. It is difficult to distinguish the thickness of the cementum on this section at this magnification. (As seen under very low power of the microscope.)

FIGURE 1

A MANUAL

OF

ORAL EMBRYOLOGY

AND

MICROSCOPIC ANATOMY

A Textbook for Students in
Dental Hygiene

By

DOROTHY PERMAR, B.S., M.S.

Associate Professor of Dentistry, (Oral Histology and Dental Anatomy),
College of Dentistry, The Ohio State University, Columbus, Ohio

Third Edition

96 ILLUSTRATIONS

LEA & FEBIGER

PHILADELPHIA

1963

Preface to the Third Edition

In the hope of partially compensating for the lack of opportunity in most Dental Hygiene Schools for students to study sections of oral tissues with a microscope, a number of photographs have been added to this edition. I want particularly to thank Dr. Duncan McConnell for instruction in photography which enabled me to make these additional pictures.

I wish to express appreciation also to Dr. Paul Kitchin for doing some critical reading, to Dr. Joseph Hunter and Mr. Ralph Ulbrich for technical assistance, to Mrs. Helen Fox for assistance in typing, and to the several teachers of Dental Hygiene students who offered helpful suggestions for this edition.

Dorothy Permar

Columbus, Ohio

Preface to the First Edition

The Dental Hygiene student must acquire a basic knowledge of the origin and structure of the tissues of the oral cavity. This is important for several reasons. First, it gives the student a basis for exercising judgment in the execution of an oral prophylaxis. An ability to visualize the structure of the oral tissues below their surface may prevent incorrect or careless performance. Second, acquaintance with normal tissue will help the student to recognize abnormal conditions which will inevitably be encountered, and will emphasize the importance of informing the dentist of these conditions. Third, a knowledge of the oral tissues will assist the Dental Hygienist in instructing patients clearly and correctly in the procedures for oral care. Fourth, an elementary knowledge concerning the embryonic development of the face and the oral cavity may give some factual information on which to base answers to patients' questions about anomalies. If it does nothing else, it will create an awareness that there is much to be learned in this field. It may even develop the prudence, too often found only associated with maturity and great wisdom, to say "I don't know" at the proper time. And fifth, but not of least importance, increased knowledge in any field of work means increased interest and enjoyment for the worker.

Dental Hygiene curriculums vary in different schools. This manual presupposes a course in general biology or in zoology. It is written with the assumption that the student understands the meaning of cells and of cell division, and that the vocabulary of biologic science is not entirely unfamiliar. It does not assume previous instruction in embryology or histology. The manual is intended for use in conjunction with lectures or discussion periods.

The order of study of the various phases of oral histology and embryology is somewhat a matter of personal preference. In teaching this subject I have found it necessary for the student to know something of the microscopic anatomy of tooth tissues before trying to visualize their embryonic development. For this reason, tooth embryology follows tooth histology. And an understanding of the development of the face and of the meaning of the three primary embryonic layers needs to precede the study of tooth development. Rather than insert the chapter on the embryology of the face and oral cavity between tooth histology and tooth embryology, this chapter is placed at the beginning.

The microscopic structures of enamel, dentin, pulp, cementum, perio-dontal membrane, bone, oral mucosa, epithelial attachment, and salivary glands are described as simply as possible. An effort has been made to avoid elaboration of details which are unnecessary for the efficient and intelligent practice of Dental Hygiene. A few of the statements made as facts may be somewhat controversial, but it seemed advisable to avoid confusing conflicts of ideas, particularly in matters not of immediate concern to the Dental Hygienist.

I am greatly indebted to Dr. Paul C. Kitchin for kindly permitting me to use his large collection of microscope slides of oral tissues. Many of the illustrations were drawn directly from these slides. Some are composite pictures of several of the slides. All of the drawings are diagrammatic and not detailed. This type of illustration was used in the belief that the beginning student often understands a simplified diagram better than a photomicrograph.

I wish to express sincere thanks to Dr. Kitchin, Dr. Hamilton Robinson, and Dr. William Lefkowitz for reading the manuscript and offering many valuable suggestions. Without their assistance, this little book would contain many more errors than it perhaps does contain. Gratitude is also due to Mrs. Marice Kersey Musgrove for special assistance with the manuscript, and to Mr. Jack Gottschalk for help in the preparation of the manuscript.

DOROTHY PERMAR

COLUMBUS, OHIO

Contents

1

Embryonic Development of the Face and Oral Cavity

THE HUMAN BODY

THE BEGINNING OF A HUMAN BODY

The life of an individual human body begins at the moment the sperm unites with the ovum and forms a fertilized egg. The egg soon divides into two cells, and then each of these again divides, making four cells. Continuing cell divisions produce a minute mass of undifferentiated cells which soon undergoes a marked change in shape and comes to resemble a thick-walled tube.

Essentially the pattern of an adult human body is that of a large tube with a small tube running through it. The outside body wall is the large tube, and the digestive tract is the small inside tube. The mouth is the cephalad (head) opening to the inside tube, and the anus is the caudad (tail) opening. The region between the two tubes—that is, between the body wall and the wall of the digestive tract—is occupied by the internal organs such as the liver, the heart, the lungs. The region within the smaller tube—that is, inside the oral cavity, the esophagus, the stomach, and the intestines—is not actually inside the body cavity: it is merely the space within the tube which runs through the body.

This pattern for the human body is established very early in embryonic life when the minute embryo changes its shape from a mass of undifferentiated cells to a thick-walled tube. The inside of this tube is the primitive digestive tract. At this early stage the mouth and the anus have not formed; the tube is closed at both ends. The thick wall of this embryonic tube is composed of *three primary embryonic layers:* the outer layer is the *ectoderm* (ecto = outside; derm = skin); the inner layer, which lines the primitive digestive tract, is the *endoderm* (endo = inside); and the layer between the ectoderm and endoderm is the *mesoderm* (meso = middle).

The entire body develops as a result of the multiplication and differentiation of the cells of the three primary embryonic layers. Cells derived from the three layers differentiate into specialized types and develop into the various tissues which form all of the organs of the body. Such widely different structures as the epithelium of the skin which covers the body, and the brain and spinal cord, are derived from the ectoderm as the cells from this layer multiply and become specialized in different ways. The endoderm gives rise to the epithelial lining of the digestive tract (excepting the oral epithelium) and the lining of the lungs, and to the liver, and to

(15)

parts of the urogenital system. Cells derived from the mesoderm produce the skeleton, the muscular system, the blood system, and parts of the urogenital system.

The epithelium of the oral cavity is derived from ectoderm. It rests upon connective tissue which is derived from mesoderm. A tooth is derived from these two primary embryonic layers: the enamel from ectoderm and the dentin, pulp, and cementum from mesoderm.

SIZE OF A HUMAN FETUS

At the end of the third week after fertilization the embryo is a tube about 3 millimeters long (approximately $\frac{1}{8}$ inch). By the end of the second month it has acquired a form recognizable as a human being. In later stages of development the size of the human fetus usually is given in terms of the crown-rump length. At the end of three months the fetus has a crown-rump length of about 56 millimeters (about $2\frac{1}{4}$ inches); and at the end of four months it has a crown-rump length of about 112 millimeters (over 4 inches). (See Fig. 2, A and B.)

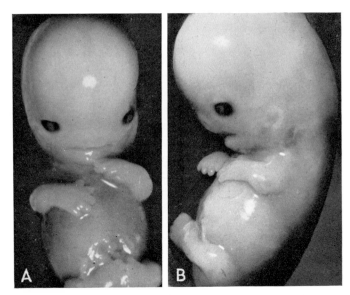

FIGURE 2, A and B. A human embryo 25 mm. long—about 8 weeks old. The head is large, making up nearly half of the body length. Compared to the size of the brain, the face appears small. The eyes are widespread; the ears are close to the neck. The nose is nearly flat. Notice the small size of the mandible. Inside of the mouth of an embryo of this age the lateral palatine processes are in a vertical position and the tongue is tall and narrow and nearly touches the lower border of the nasal septum (Fig. 6A). (Courtesy Dr. Rudy Melfi.)

THE FACE AND ORAL CAVITY

EARLY DEVELOPMENT

The human face starts to develop during the third week in utero when the embryo is a tube made up of ectoderm, mesoderm, and endoderm and is closed at both ends. Development of the face begins with the establishment of the oral cavity. The formation of the early oral cavity, or primi-

PLATE I

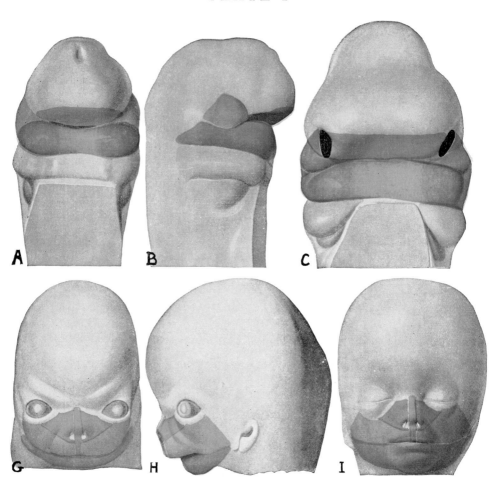

Development of the Human Face

A and **B**. Human embryo, third week: Maxillary processes have developed from the first branchial arch. Stomodeum has formed. Frontal process (which here is blue) is undivided. Second and third branchial arches are visible. Depression on top of head is the neuropore.
C. Fourth week: Nasal pits have divided the frontal process into the median nasal process (blue) and the right and left lateral nasal processes (pink).

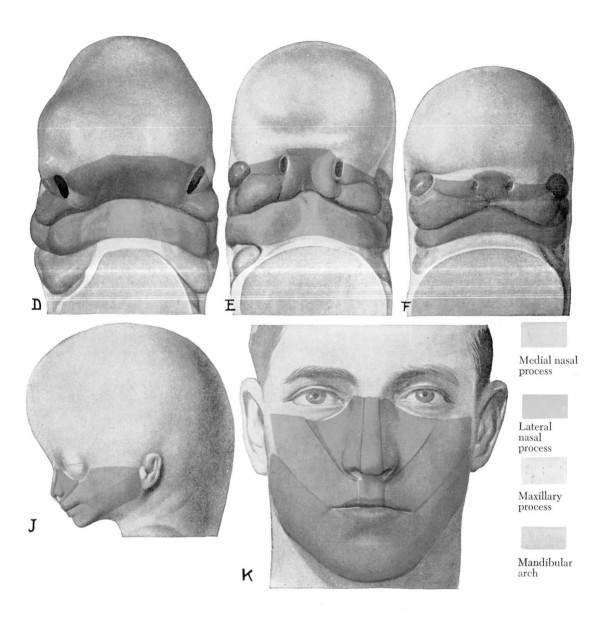

Medial nasal process

Lateral nasal process

Maxillary process

Mandibular arch

D. Fifth week: Globular processes have appeared and are fused with the maxillary processes. **E.** Sixth week: Due to differential growth, median nasal process is now relatively narrow. Eyes are on lateral border of face. **F.** Seventh week: Median nasal process is relatively narrow. Eyes are now anterior in position. **G** and **H.** Eighth week: Lidless eyes are on anterior of face. The mandible is small. Nose protrudes slightly. Ears are low on side of head. **I** and **J.** Twelfth week: Eyelids closed. Ears appear higher. Mandible further developed. **K.** Adult face: Derivatives of median nasal process are blue; of lateral nasal processes are pink; of maxillary processes are green; of mandibular processes are yellow.

(Orban's *Oral Histology and Embryology,* courtesy of the C. V. Mosby Co.)

tive mouth, starts as an invagination of the ectoderm at the cephalic end (head end) of the closed embryonic tube. The ectoderm in this area dips in until it meets and unites with the endoderm of the primitive digestive tract (Fig. 3). The intervening mesoderm in this area disappears. The cavity formed by the invagination of the ectoderm is the *primitive mouth.** The primitive mouth is separated from the *primitive digestive tract* by a membrane composed of the united ectoderm and endoderm. This is the

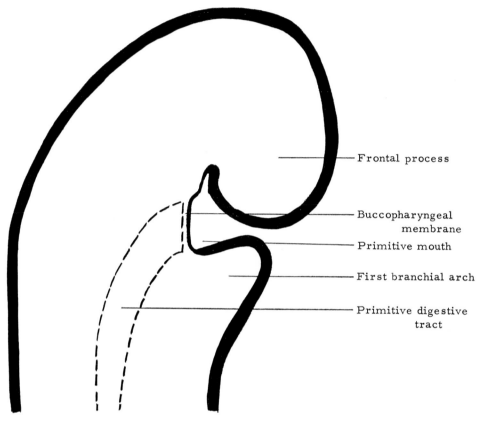

Frontal process

Buccopharyngeal
  membrane

Primitive mouth

First branchial arch

Primitive digestive
  tract

FIGURE 3.—A diagrammatic illustration of a median sagital section through the head of a human embryo at the end of the third week in utero. About 3 mm.

buccopharyngeal membrane. It lies approximately in the region that will be occupied by the palatine tonsils. The location of the buccopharyngeal membrane makes it evident that the primitive oral cavity is lined with ectoderm, although the lining of the primitive digestive tract caudad to the buccopharyngeal membrane is derived from endoderm.

During the fourth week in utero the buccopharyngeal membrane ruptures, establishing communication between the primitive mouth and the primitive digestive tract. Further development of the face centers about the mouth.

Above the opening of the primitive mouth a large bulge is produced by the growth of the forebrain (Figs. 3 and 4). The ectoderm and mesoderm

* Another name for *primitive mouth* is *stomodeum.*

which cover the forebrain develop into an embryonic structure called the *frontal process*. The frontal process gives rise to the structures of the upper part of the face.

Below the opening of the primitive mouth in the region of the future neck, five paired *branchial arches* are formed. These are ordinarily designated as branchial arches I, II, III, IV, and V (Fig. 4). They are homologous to the gill arches in fish. In the development of the human face and oral cavity only the first three branchial arches play a part

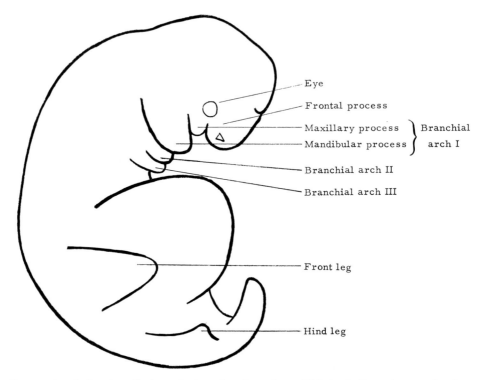

FIGURE 4.—A drawing of a lateral view of a pig embryo. This is similar to human development at this stage. Branchial arches IV and V are not visible here.

Branchial arch I is destined to develop into the mandible and a large part of the maxilla. Branchial arches II and III join the first branchial arch in the development of the tongue.

By the end of the fourth week in utero the primitive mouth is established and the buccopharyngeal membrane has ruptured. Above the primitive mouth is the frontal process and below the primitive mouth is the first branchial arch (Fig. 3). The entire face and all of the structures of the oral cavity with the exception of the posterior part of the tongue are now going to develop from these two primordia (beginnings): the *frontal process* and the *first branchial arch*.

THE DEVELOPMENT OF THE FACE

As soon as the primitive oral cavity is established and the frontal process and the first branchial arch become distinguishable, small buds develop on the upper border of the right and left ends of the first branchial arch (Figs. 4 and 5). These buds are the *maxillary processes*. The original lower portions of the first branchial arch are now called the right and left *mandibular processes*. The mandibular processes will form the mandible and the lower part of the sides of the face. The maxillary processes are destined to give rise to the upper part of the cheeks, the sides of the upper lip, and a large part of the palate and maxillary arch. (See Plate I).

After the mandibular processes and the maxillary processes have formed, growth of the lower part of the face is retarded and the frontal process

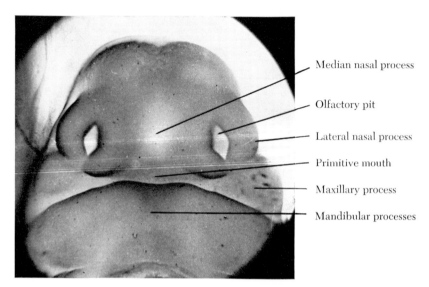

Median nasal process

Olfactory pit

Lateral nasal process

Primitive mouth

Maxillary process

Mandibular processes

FIGURE 5.—A photograph of the face of a pig embryo of about 12 mm. At this stage of development the pig face and the human face are very much alike.

starts a rapid development. On its lower border the frontal process develops a pair of invaginations, the right and left *olfactory pits*, which are the future openings into the nose (Fig. 5 and Plate I). The olfactory pits divide the lower part of the frontal process into three parts: a center portion called the *median nasal process* and two lateral portions called the *lateral nasal processes*. The lateral nasal processes become the sides of the nose. The median nasal process forms the center and tip of the nose. Later, an ingrowth from the center of the nose forms the nasal septum (the division between the right and left nasal chambers). On its lower border the median nasal process develops a pair of bulges, called the *globular processes* (Plate I, D). The globular processes are not separated, but remain as a single median structure which grows downward so that it extends below the olfactory pits and lies between the maxillary processes. It forms the center of the upper lip (the philtrum). The maxillary processes form the sides of the upper lip. During the second month in utero the globular processes fuse with the right and left maxillary processes, the lines of fusion being beneath the nasal openings (Fig. 7, A). Thus the three

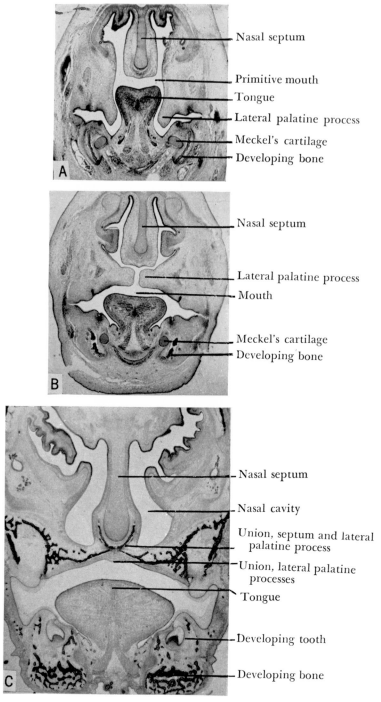

Nasal septum

Primitive mouth

Tongue

Lateral palatine process

Meckel's cartilage

Developing bone

Nasal septum

Lateral palatine process

Mouth

Meckel's cartilage

Developing bone

Nasal septum

Nasal cavity

Union, septum and lateral palatine process

Union, lateral palatine processes

Tongue

Developing tooth

Developing bone

FIGURE 6.—Frontal sections through the head of 3 pigs showing progressive stages in development of the palate. This is similar to human palatal development. *A.* The vertical position of the lateral palatine processes and the position of the tongue which nearly touches the lower border of the nasal septum are similar to the condition in an 8-week-old human embryo (Fig. 2). *B.* The shortening and broadening of the tongue, the horizontal position of the palatine processes, and their lack of union at the midline are similar to the condition in a 9-week-old human embryo. *C.* In a human fetus of 12 weeks, as in this pig fetus, the palatine processes have fused with each other and with the lower border of the nasal septum. The oral cavity and the nasal cavity are now separated by the roof of the mouth.

sections of the upper lip become a single structure. These fusions are completed before the end of the second month *in utero*.

THE DEVELOPMENT OF THE PALATE

By the second half of the second month in utero the palate has started to develop. The maxillary processes each produce a *lateral palatine process* inside the mouth, and the globular processes produce the *premaxilla*. The lateral palatine processes are somewhat like shelves growing from the sides of the mouth toward the midline and downward (Fig. 6*A*). The down-

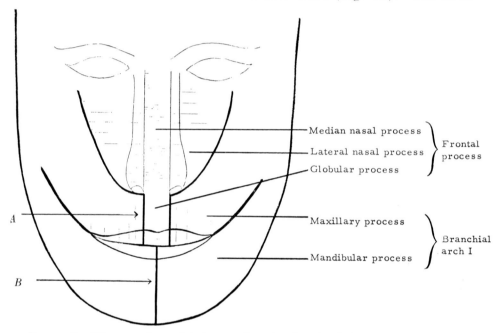

FIGURE 7.—Diagram of an adult human face showing the derivations of its parts from the frontal process and the first branchial arch. *A* and *B* indicate the locations where clefts sometimes occur in the upper lip and in the mandible.

ward direction of growth is due to the presence of a relatively large and thick embryonic tongue which lies between the lateral palatine processes and almost touches the lower border of the nasal septum. The premaxilla grows inward from the oral side of the globular processes and becomes a small triangular area in the anterior part of the roof of the mouth and that part of the maxillary arch which usually bears the incisor teeth (Fig. 8).

At the beginning of the third month in utero there is a considerable growth of the mandible, a structure which to this point has lagged in development. This mandibular growth makes room for the tongue to drop down from its position between the lateral palatine processes (Fig. 6*B*). With the tongue out of the way the lateral palatine processes assume a horizontal position and meet in the center line of the roof of the mouth where they fuse with each other and with the nasal septum (Fig. 6*C*). At their anterior borders the lateral palatine processes fuse with the premaxilla (Fig. 8).

The fusion of the lateral palatine processes with each other and with the premaxilla results in a Y-shaped pattern of fusion in the roof of the mouth (Fig. 8). The palatal fusions are normally completed by the end of the third month in utero.

These palatal fusions are fusions of soft tissue, not of bone. The first evidence of bone formation in the area of the forming palate is seen during the eighth week in utero when the lateral palatine processes are still in a vertical position. At this time specialized bone-forming cells (osteoblasts) become differentiated in the mesenchyme. By the end of the third month,

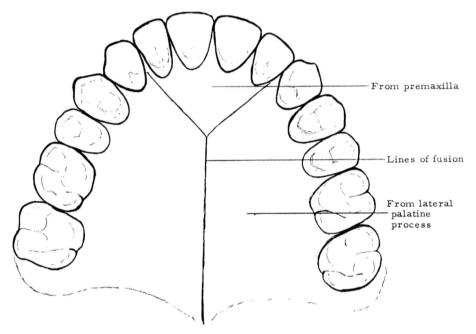

FIGURE 8.—Drawing of the oral surface of a human maxilla.
The Y-shaped lines of embryonic fusion are indicated.

when the soft palatal structures have completed their fusion, there is considerable bone formed in the palate, but the bones of the right and left sides of the palate are not together at the midline. A separation of the *bones* of the right and left sides of the palate still exists at the end of the fourth month in utero.

The embryonic derivations of the structures of the oral cavity may be briefly summarized: The oral structures are derived mostly from the first branchial arch; only the premaxilla develops from the frontal process. The rest of the hard palate and all of the soft palate develop from the maxillary processes, which are buds from the first branchial arch. The mandible develops from the first branchial arch.

THE DEVELOPMENT OF THE TONGUE

During the second month in utero the first, second, and third branchial arches together give rise to the tongue. The tongue develops on the ventral wall of the upper part of the throat. It has been described as a sac of mucous membrane into which a mass of muscle has grown. As it develops the tongue ascends into the mouth and is directed anteriorly toward the opening of the mouth. By the beginning of the third month in utero the tongue has acquired a recognizable form.

SUMMARY

A summary of the derivations of the structures of the face and oral cavity is presented in the following outline:

I. From the *Frontal Process* are derived
    1. Median nasal process, which gives rise to
        a. Center and tip of nose
        b. Nasal septum
        c. Globular processes, which give rise to
            (1) Philtrum of upper lip
            (2) Premaxilla
    2. Lateral nasal processes, which form
        a. Sides of nose
        b. Infraorbital areas

II. From *Branchial Arch I* are derived
    1. Mandibular processes, which give rise to
        a. Mandible
        b. Lower parts of face
        c. Anterior part of tongue
    2. Maxillary processes, which give rise to
        a. Lateral palatine processes (*i.e.*, all of palate and maxillary alveolar arch excepting premaxilla)
        b. Upper part of cheeks
        c. Sides of upper lip

III. From *Branchial Arches II and III* are derived portions of the posterior part of the tongue

ANOMALIES

An anomaly is a marked deviation from the normal standard. Anomalies of the face and oral cavity sometimes result from failure of fusion of, or from arrested development of some of the parts.

Cleft lip is the result of failure of proper fusion between the center portion of the upper lip and one or both sides of the lip—that is, between the globular processes and one or both of the maxillary processes (Fig. 7, *A*). This defect may occur either unilaterally or bilaterally, with or without accompanying cleft palate. If cleft lip occurs, it will be evident before the end of the second month in utero because by this time the fusion of the structures concerned has normally taken place.

Cleft of the palate may occur at any place along the lines of fusion of the hard or soft palate. Normally fusion occurs in the roof of the mouth between the right and left palatine processes and between the palatine processes and the premaxilla (Fig. 8). This makes a Y-shaped pattern of fusion in the roof of the mouth. Failure of fusion may be of any degree of severity, ranging from a scarcely noticeable bifurcation (division into two branches) of the uvula to a complete lack of fusion of all structures involved. Any severe cleft of the palate results in direct communication between the oral cavity and the nasal cavity. Where failure of fusion of the lateral palatine processes and the premaxilla results in a cleft of the alveolar ridge, the maxillary lateral incisor tooth is affected. The lateral incisor may be medial to the cleft, it may be distal to the cleft, it may be missing entirely, or there may be two lateral incisors, one on either side of the cleft. Fusion of the intraoral structures is normally completed by the end of the third month *in utero*. Therefore, if cleft palate occurs it will be evident by the end of the third month of intrauterine development. Research conducted in Pennsylvania in 1942 indicated that 1 child in every 800 born in that state had some type of cleft palate, cleft lip, or both.

Another defect which may occur is an *oblique facial cleft*. This cleft extends from the eye to the lower corner of the nose. Its cause is sometimes said to be trauma to the face of the fetus.

A condition called *macrostomia* (large mouth) may result from insufficient fusion of the maxillary processes and the mandibular processes at the corners of the embryonic mouth.

A *cleft of the chin* may occur in the center line as a result of a cleft between the right and left mandibular processes (Fig. 7, B).

2

Introduction to Histology

GENERAL HISTOLOGY

THE NATURE OF HISTOLOGY

Histology is the science of tissues (histo = tissue; ology = the science of).
Botanists study plant tissues; zoologists study animal tissues. Students
of human histology study the tissues of the human body; and those having
a particular interest in Dentistry study especially the tissues of the oral
cavity.

A *tissue* is sometimes defined as a group of more or less similar cells
with intercellular substance and tissue fluid, combined in a characteristic
manner and performing a particular function. Some examples of human
tissues are muscle, bone, blood, epithelium of the skin and of the mucous
membrane, connective tissue of the skin and of the mucous membrane,
and the pulp of a tooth. The hard components of a tooth, enamel, dentin,
and cementum, are also tissues, although enamel and dentin have excep-
tional characteristics.

Tissues vary greatly in appearance and in structure. Some are hard
(bone); some are soft (muscle). Some are sturdy and withstand wear and
injury (surface layer of the skin); and some are delicate and serve as
linings (lining of the respiratory tract). Some are secretory in function
(salivary gland tissue); and some are nutritive in function (blood).

HOW TISSUES ARE STUDIED

Microscopic examination of the structure of tissues started over 100
years ago, and study has been extended and developed as improvements
have been made in the construction of microscopes and in the techniques
of tissue preparation. Usually tissues must be stained in some manner in
order that their different components may be seen clearly with a microscope. Sometimes dyes are injected into the blood stream of a living
animal, and the tissues which have taken up the stain from the blood are
subsequently removed from the animal and cut into thin sections. Or
tissues may be grown in artificial nutrient medium in a glass tube, and
their growth and development observed from hour to hour or from day to
day. The most usual method of tissue preparation is probably that of
removing a small piece of tissue from the body, embedding it in paraffin,
sectioning it, and staining it.

Let us suppose, for example, that a dentist wants to examine the microscopic structure of the soft tissue surrounding the teeth. A small piece

of this gingival tissue is carefully removed from the mouth with a sharp instrument and is immediately placed in a bottle containing 10 per cent formalin. In this solution it is sent to a microtechnique laboratory. When the specimen is received in the laboratory, it is dehydrated in absolute alcohol, allowed to stand in xylene, and then placed in a dish of melted paraffin which is kept in a warming oven. In a few hours the paraffin will have completely permeated the tissue. The paraffin and tissue are then poured into a small paper container. Hardened in cool water, the paraffin becomes a firm block which contains the specimen in its center. The paraffin block is then cut into sections (slices) with an instrument called a microtome. Each paraffin section is about 8 microns thick (approximately $\frac{8}{25000}$ inch), and has in its center, of course, a section of the embedded specimen which is the same in thickness. The paraffin sections are arranged on glass microscope slides, with egg albumin used as an adhesive. The slides are then passed through xylene which dissolves away the embedding paraffin, leaving the thin section of tissue attached to the slide. In order that the structure of the tissue may be studied, it is necessary now to pass the slides through appropriate tissue stains.

There are innumerable kinds of tissue stains. One of the common combinations of stains is hematoxylin and eosin. When the slides bearing the sections of tissue are immersed in the hematoxylin the nuclei of the cells will take up the stain and become deep blue. Subsequent immersion in the eosin stain will cause the cytoplasm of the epithelial cells to become a pinkish color and the intercellular substance of the connective tissue to become very pink. Stains other than hematoxylin and eosin are used to bring out different tissue structures. After they are stained the tissue sections are covered with a small, very thin cover glass. In this way the slides are permanently preserved.

Specimens which contain calcified tissue such as bone and teeth must be decalcified in a weak acid before they can be cut with the sharp knife of the microtome. The decalcification process is the removal (dissolving) of the mineral material from the organic material of a tissue. Five per cent nitric acid is often used for this purpose. As a result of this decalcification process, changes are inevitable in certain tissues. Tooth enamel, for instance, is usually entirely lost when a tooth is allowed to stand in acid. Tooth enamel is about 96 per cent mineral material and only 4 per cent organic material and water. When the mineral material is removed by the acid, the delicate organic portion of the enamel is mechanically washed away unless special techniques for its preservation are employed. Other kinds of calcified tissues retain their form when they are decalcified. Dentin and bone, because they contain a much greater proportion of organic material, are not thus destroyed when the mineral material is removed in the process of decalcification. Completely decalcified dentin or bone will retain its original shape, although it may be easily pierced with a needle.

The enamel of a tooth may be preserved for study if instead of using the decalcifying, embedding, and sectioning procedures the tooth is merely ground down to one thin section. This is done on a lathe with a revolving stone. With this technique it is not difficult to obtain a tooth section less than 20 microns thick. Specimens of teeth prepared in this way are referred to as *ground sections*. Ground sections are mounted on glass slides and covered with a cover glass in the same way that other types of sections are preserved.

COMPONENTS OF A TISSUE

Tissues are made up of *cells, intercellular substance*, and *tissue fluid*.

A *cell* is a unit of living substance (protoplasm). Usually it is made up of cytoplasm and a nucleus. A cell may exist as an individual, as in such unicellular animals as an ameba or a paramecium. Or a cell may be part of a tissue of a large animal or plant and be dependent upon other cells

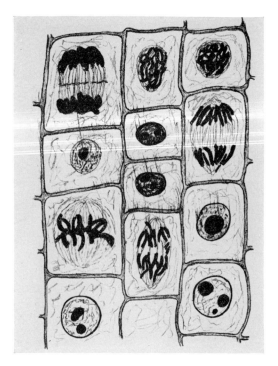

FIGURE 9.—Drawing of a small area in the tip of an onion root showing the division of some of the cells. (High power magnification.)

for existence. When we think of a cell we often visualize a cuboidal or oblong block of cytoplasm with a limiting membrane around its surface and a round nucleus in its center. This regular, picturesque type of cell is often found in plants. The cells of an onion root tip, for instance, are cuboidal or oblong in shape, have a clearly defined nucleus and cytoplasm, and a regularly shaped cell wall (Fig. 9).

But cells show an almost infinite variation in size, shape, and structure. In animals the largest of all cells is an ovum: a chicken egg is a very large single cell; and the human ovum, although measuring only about 1/250 inch in diameter, is still a relatively large cell (Fig. 10). In contrast to these cells, the red blood cells circulating in the human blood stream have a diameter of about 7/25,000 inch. The structure of human red blood cells is unusual in that these cells have lost their nuclei. White blood cells, on the other hand, contain one or several nuclei (Fig. 11). Muscle cells are distinctive because their cytoplasm has the power of strong contraction (Figs. 13, *E* and *F*). Fat cells contain large amounts of fat, which

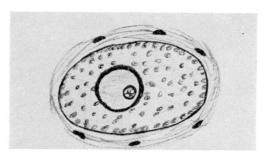

FIGURE 10.—Drawing of a human ovum enclosed in its follicle.
(High power magnification.)

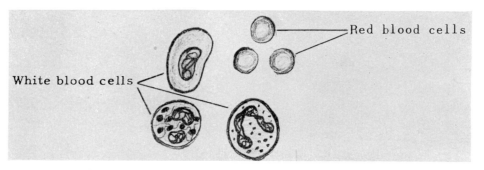

FIGURE 11.—Drawing of some cells of human blood as seen
under the oil immersion objective of the microscope.

FIGURE 12.—Drawing of fat cells. (High power magnification.)

push the nuclei away from the center of the cells and against the cell walls (Fig. 12). From this brief discussion it is clear that there are many kinds of cells, and later it will be seen that these different kinds of cells along with varying kinds and amounts of intercellular substance and different amounts of tissue fluid determine the nature of the various kinds of tissues.

Intercellular substance is a product of living cells and is distributed among the cells in all of the tissues of the body. It holds the cells together and provides a medium for the passing of nutrients and of waste materials from capillaries to cells and from cells to capillaries. The amount and kind of intercellular substance differ in different tissues. In some human tissues, such as bone, intercellular substance is the predominent element. In other human tissues, such as the epithelium which makes up the surface of the skin, intercellular substance is small in amount and the cellular elements predominate. Intercellular substance occurs in two forms: one form is *fibrous* in nature, and the other is *amorphous* in nature (a = without; morphous = form).

Tissue fluid is that part of the blood plasma which can diffuse through the walls of capillaries. In the tissue fluid nutrients are carried out through capillary walls to the surrounding intercellular substance and thence to the cells; and waste products of the cells are returned in the same manner from the intercellular substance to the capillaries. Tissue fluid may be present in a tissue in relatively small proportions, as in the epithelium of the surface of the skin; or it may form a large proportion of the tissue, as in blood. The tissue fluid of epithelium, of bone, and of other tissues is, of course, derived from blood.

CLASSIFICATION OF TISSUES

In their gross and microscopic appearance, and in their function, tissues vary so widely that the beginning student may well feel that there is little or no relationship among them. This seeming confusion grows less, however, when it is discovered that for purposes of easier study and better understanding histologists have developed a classification for tissues. Tissues are alike in that they are made up of cells, intercellular substance, and tissue fluid. Tissues differ in the form and number of cells, in the type and amount of intercellular substance, and in the amount of tissue fluid. It is on the similarities and differences of tissues that the histologist has based his classification.

Human tissues have been assorted into *four primary groups: epithelial tissue, connective tissue, muscle tissue,* and *nervous tissue.* The tissues of each of these primary groups have certain major, fundamental characteristics in common. But there are also differences within the groups; and so each of the four primary groups has been subdivided. The subdivisions are based on structural differences which clearly distinguish one tissue from another.

A brief classification of human tissues is presented in Table 1.

Tissues are combined in characteristic ways to form organs, such as heart, lungs, liver, bones, skin, tongue; and organs are combined in characteristic ways to form organisms, such as the human body.

Let us consider the tongue as an organ. The tongue is made up of a combination of epithelial tissue, connective tissue, muscle tissue, and nervous tissue, all of which are interdependent in the functioning of the organ (Fig. 14). Epithelial tissue comprises the surface of the tongue and serves as a protective covering. Beneath the epithelium is connective tissue which supplies both support and nourishment; and beneath this connective tissue layer are strong muscles which produce movement of the organ. Nerves of the tongue supply both motor and sensory functions.

Another organ of the human body is the skin. Skin is made up of a combination of epithelial tissue, connective tissue, and nerves. The skin covers and protects other body organs, such as bones and muscles. Bones support the body, and muscles move the bones and other organs under the direction of the nervous system which supplies the impulses. The entire organism is nourished by blood pumped through the pipe line of blood vessels by the cardiac muscle, which is the chief tissue of the heart.

TABLE 1.—CLASSIFICATION OF TISSUES

Epithelial Tissue
1. Surface cells of covering and of lining membranes (as of skin and of mucous membranes)
2. Glandular tissue

Connective Tissue
1. Fibrous (as in skin beneath the epithelium)
2. Loose areolar (as in thin membranes between various layers of tissue)
3. Adipose (fat)
4. Hemopoietic (= blood-forming: bone marrow, lymphatic tissue)
5. Cartilage
6. Bone

Nervous Tissue
1. Tissue of central nervous system
2. Tissue of peripheral nervous system

Muscle Tissue
1. Smooth involuntary (as in wall of intestines)
2. Striated voluntary (as in skeletal muscle)
3. Striated involuntary (heart muscle)

EPITHELIAL TISSUE

Epithelial tissue is distributed widely throughout the body and has many different kinds of structure. It occurs as a covering or a lining tissue making up both the surface layer of the skin and the surface layer of the mucous membranes which line body cavities such as the mouth, the stomach, and the intestines. Epithelial tissue also gives rise to several organs during embryonic development. Of epithelial origin in the developing embryo are the highly specialized cells of such organs as the pancreas, the liver, the thyroid gland, and the salivary glands. Also in certain locations in the upper and lower jaws epithelial tissue becomes differentiated into structures called the *enamel organs* which, located deep in the jaw, produce the enamel on the crowns of developing teeth (Chapter 11).

The various kinds of epithelial tissues are similar to one another in that they have a proportionally large number of cells and very little intercellular substance. They are dissimilar in many ways, their structure in different locations in the body being fortunately adapted to the functions which they perform.

For purposes of description histologists have classified epithelial tissues into two major groups and several subgroups:

1. *Surface cells of covering and lining membranes*

                                   ⎧ Squamous

a. Simple   ⎨ Cuboidal

                                     ⎩ Columnar

  b. Pseudostratified columnar

                                   ⎧ Squamous

                                   | Cuboidal

c. Stratified   ⎨ Columnar

                                   ⎩ Transitional

2. *Glandular Tissue*

    a. Endocrine glands, *e.g.*, thyroid
    b. Exocrine glands, *e.g.*, salivary glands
    c. Mixed endocrine and exocrine, *e.g.*, liver, pancreas

All types of epithelium will not be discussed here. The enamel organ, which is neither a covering or a lining membrane nor a gland, will be considered in the chapter dealing with the development of teeth. The salivary glands will be described in the chapter on the oral mucous membrane and the salivary glands. The endocrine glands while important physiologically to the development and health of the structures of the oral cavity are of little importance to the dental hygienist so far as their histologic composition is concerned. These glands will not, therefore, be discussed in this text. The types of epithelium which make up the surface cells of covering and lining membranes will be considered briefly.

Epithelial cells of covering and lining membranes are not all alike in shape and arrangement. The *shape* of epithelial cells is described by the words squamous, cuboidal, and columnar; and the *arrangement* of epithelial cells is described by the words simple, stratified, and pseudostratified. The word *squamous* means scale-like, or flat; and *squamous epithelial cells* are flat cells. *Cuboidal epithelial cells* are roughly cube-shaped; and *columnar epithelial cells* are tall and narrow. When the arrangement of epithelial cells is in a single layer the tissue is said to be *simple epithelium*. When epithelial cells are arranged in several layers the tissue is called *stratified epithelium* (stratified = in layers). The word *pseudostratified* is applied to an arrangement of columnar epithelial cells in which the cells appear to be stratified but are actually in a single layer (pseudo = false).

All *simple epithelium* is very delicate in structure. Simple epithelium is found only in those areas of the body which are subjected to little or no friction in functional use. *Simple squamous epithelium* (a single layer of flat epithelial cells) is found lining the inside of the walls of blood vessels (Fig. 13, *A*). *Simple cuboidal epithelium* (a single layer of cuboidal epithelial cells) is found in the covering epithelium of the ovary (Fig. 13, *B*). *Simple columnar epithelium* (a single layer of columnar epithelial cells) lines the cervix of the uterus (Fig. 13, *C*).

Pseudostratified columnar epithelium (Fig. 13, *D*) makes up the epithelial part of the mucous membrane which lines the upper respiratory tract: the maxillary sinuses, the nasal cavity, and the trachea. This epithelium is actually composed of a single layer of columnar epithelial cells; but because in some of the cells the nucleus is located near the base of the cell, while in other cells the nucleus is located nearer the outer end, this epithelium has the appearance of being made up of two or three layers of cells. In the upper respiratory tract the pseudostratified columnar epithelium is supplied with *cilia* and with *goblet cells* (Fig. 13, D). Cilia are minute, hair-like projections which cover the surface ends of the columnar cells and act as dust catchers, or filters, for the air breathed in through the nose. Goblet cells are modified epithelial cells which are interspersed among the other columnar cells and which secrete substances that keep the tissue surface of the nose and sinuses moist.

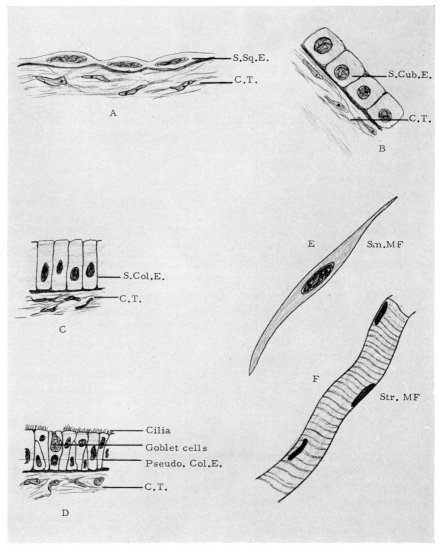

FIGURE 13.—Diagrammatic drawings of some different types of cells. *A*. Simple squamous epithelium (*S. Sq. E.*) resting on connective tissue (*C.T.*). *B*. Simple cuboidal epithelium (*S. Cub. E.*) resting on connective tissue (*C.T.*). *C*. Simple columnar epithelium (*S. Col. E.*) resting on connective tissue (*C.T.*). *D*. Pseudostratified columnar epithelium (*Pseudo. Col. E.*) resting on connective tissue (*C.T.*). *E*. A smooth muscle fiber. *F*. A striated muscle fiber.

Stratified epithelium consists of cells which are similar in shape to cells of simple epithelium, but which are arranged so that they are from 2 or 3 to many layers deep. *Stratified cuboidal epithelium* and *stratified columnar epithelium* occur as the lining of some of the larger ducts of glands, such as the large ducts of the major salivary glands. The stratified epithelial cells which line the urinary bladder change in shape from round to flat,

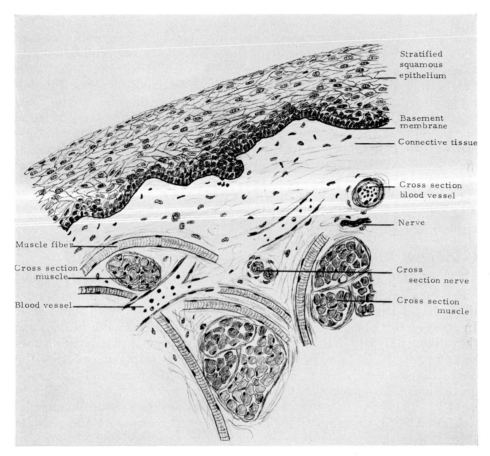

FIGURE 14.—Diagrammatic drawing of a section of tissue taken from the under side of the human tongue. This section illustrates the way in which tissues are combined. (High power magnification.)

depending on whether the bladder is empty or full, and this epithelium is therefore described as *stratified transitional epithelium*. Stratified epithelium is more resistant to hard use than the simple types of epithelium. By far the most sturdy of all kinds of epithelia is *stratified squamous epithelium* which is found covering all surfaces of the body which are routinely subjected to considerable wear and tear.

Stratified squamous epithelium (Fig. 14) makes up both the surface of the skin and the surface of the mucous membrane of the oral cavity. In both of these locations the epithelium is composed of many layers of cells. The deepest layer of these epithelial cells rests on a fine structure called the *basement membrane* which separates the epithelial tissue from its underlying connective tissue. The epithelial cells of the deepest layer, called *basal cells*, are not flat in shape but are somewhat cuboidal and often show cell division. As these basal cells multiply, some cells are gradually moved toward the outside surface, becoming flatter in shape as they approach the surface and finally becoming dead cells. On some areas of the oral cavity the flat, dead epithelial cells on the surface are sloughed off as they are replaced from below. On other areas of the oral cavity, and on the skin, these dead surface cells are not quickly sloughed off. Instead they lose their nuclei and their cell boundaries and become converted into a very tough, resistant surface layer which is called the *keratinized layer* (Fig. 66). This keratinized layer, of course, gradually wears off and is replaced from beneath as a result of continued cell division in the basal cell layer. The most heavily keratinized epithelium of the body is found on the palms of the hands and on the soles of the feet, particularly if these areas have been subjected to hard use and are calloused. More about nonkeratinized and keratinized epithelium will be learned in the study of the oral mucosa.

Covering and lining epithelial tissue does not contain blood vessels; it receives its nourishment via the blood vessels contained in the connective tissue which surrounds or underlies it.

CONNECTIVE TISSUE

The tissues which have been classified together as connective tissue differ from epithelial tissues basically in that they are made up of a relatively larger amount of intercellular substance and relatively fewer cells. In spite of this characteristic which connective tissues have in common they differ so greatly in form and in function that at first glance they sometimes appear to be unrelated. Connective tissue (fibrous) underlies the epithelium of the skin and the epithelium of the oral mucosa and also makes up tendons and ligaments. Connective tissue (areolar) attaches skin to muscle. Connective tissue (fat) stores food. Connective tissue (hemopoietic) forms blood. Connective tissue (cartilage) gives support and permits skeletal growth. Connective tissue (bone) supports the body.

Fibrous connective tissue is found throughout the body. In its most dense form it makes up tendons and ligaments. In a less dense form it is the connective tissue which underlies the epithelial part of skin and of mucous membranes (Figs. 14 and 66). Like other tissues, fibrous connective tissue is made up of cells and intercellular substance, and the intercellular substance is of two kinds: fibrillar and amorphous. The fibrillar component of the intercellular substance is the predominent element.

The fibers of fibrous connective tissue are probably produced by the cells of the tissue which are called *fibroblasts* (blast = germ, builder). The individual fibers are made up of minute fibrils. Special staining techniques used on histologic sections reveal that the fibers are not all alike, some being *collagenous fibers* and others *elastic fibers*. These two types of fibers are distributed in different proportions in different kinds of fibrous connective tissue.

Suspended along with the fibers in the all-encompassing amorphous substance are the various kinds of cells of the fibrous connective tissue. Proportionally the most numerous type of cell is the *fibroblast*. Special tissue preparation will show also the presence of other types of cells, some of which are capable of becoming defense cells when the tissue suffers injury or bacterial infection.

Areolar connective tissue is seen during any gross dissection of a mammal where skin is attached to muscles, muscles to muscles, or where internal organs are held together by membranes of connective tissue. These tissue membranes, called *fascia*, are made up of areolar connective tissue and fat tissue. The areolar connective tissue is composed of a relatively small number of cells and of a very loose and thin network of fibrous intercellular substance, all held together by a large amount of amorphous intercellular substance.

Fat tissue is distributed throughout the body among the soft tissues and in the marrow cavities of bones, and is found more or less generously concentrated in certain parts of the body beneath the skin. It is composed of specialized connective tissue cells, called *fat cells* (Fig. 12), which are held together by fibrous intercellular substance. Fat cells are capable of storing fat. They may become so filled with fat that the cytoplasm is pressed into a thin layer around the periphery of the cell, and the nucleus is crowded against the side of the cell.

Hemopoietic tissue (hemo = blood; poietic = to make) not only produces blood cells which are added to the circulating blood, but removes worn out blood cells from the blood stream. In the adult, hemopoietic tissue occurs in two different forms: as *red bone marrow* and as *lymphatic tissue*. In the human fetus, red bone marrow is found in nearly all of the bones; but in the adult, the marrow in many of the bones has become transformed into so-called *yellow bone marrow* (Fig. 65) which is largely fat. Certain bones, however, such as the vault of the skull, the ribs, the sternum, the bodies of vertebræ, retain the red bone marrow throughout adult life. Yellow bone marrow in other bones can be converted into hemopoietic red marrow in circumstances of emergency.

Red bone marrow consists of a fibrillar meshwork of intercellular substance throughout which are scattered many cells which have the potentiality of differentiating into several kinds of blood cells. Red bone marrow produces *red blood cells* and also certain kinds of white blood cells called *granular leukocytes* (Fig. 11), which are white blood cells that have granules in the cytoplasm (basophils, neutrophils, eosinophils).

Lymphatic tissue is composed of fibrillar intercellular substance and scattered undifferentiated cells. Some of these undifferentiated cells are capable of becoming differentiated into certain kinds of white blood cells, chiefly *lymphocytes*. Conspicuous areas of lymphatic tissue are seen in several places around the oral cavity: the palatine tonsils, which are located between the oral cavity and the pharynx; the pharyngeal tonsils, which are located on the posterior wall of the pharynx; and the lingual tonsils, which are located on the posterior part of the dorsum of the tongue. Lymphatic tissue is found also in other parts of the body.

In *cartilage* the most conspicuous component of the tissue is the amorphous intercellular substance, which in gross examination resembles a firm gel. Fibers, which may be made visible by special histologic preparation of tissue sections, are scattered throughout the amorphous intercellular substance. The cells of cartilage, called *chondrocytes*, occupy spaces, called *lacunæ*, in the intercellular substance. Nutrients are transmitted to the cells through the intercellular substance. Cartilage exists as a noncalcified tissue.

A large part of the skeleton of the human fetus is first constructed in cartilage, which seems to act as a pattern for the developing bone tissue. The arm and leg bones, for example, are first formed in cartilage, which is resorbed as bone tissue develops to replace it. While bone replaces most cartilage in the human skeleton at an early stage, cartilage persists in some places for years. At the ends of the long bones the presence of cartilage throughout childhood and adolescence permits growth in the length of the bones. In adults cartilage comprises parts of the nose, larynx, trachea, and ear. Cartilage tissue contains no nerves or blood vessels.

Bone is a calcified connective tissue (Fig. 57). Bone contains a large amount of dense fibrous intercellular substance. The fibrils are of course surrounded by amorphous intercellular substance. In the amorphous substance mineral salts are deposited in solution as the bone is developing. As the bone matures, these mineral salts crystalize out of solution and the bone becomes a calcified tissue. The cells of bone, called *osteocytes*, occupy spaces known as *lacunæ* in the hard intercellular substance. More will be learned in a later chapter about the microscopic picture of bone tissue.

Nervous Tissue

Nervous tissue, which comprises the total nervous system, is made up of nerve cells and a tissue which supports them. Nerve cells are called *neurons* and they are like other cells in that they have a nucleus and a cytoplasm. However, they are highly specialized, that is different from other cells, in that they have to a high degree the properties of reacting to stimuli (irritability) and of transmitting waves of excitation from the point where the stimulus is applied (conductivity). These waves of excitation, or *nerve impulses* as they are called, are transmitted through the cytoplasm of the neuron which is peculiarly adapted to this function.

The nervous system consists of two chief divisions: the *central nervous system* (the brain and spinal cord) and the *peripheral nervous system* (nerves associated with the various other organs of the body). The gross appearance and the histologic structure of the nervous tissue in these two divisions are very different. The tissue of the central nervous system is extremely soft due to the absence of connective tissue as a supporting tissue for the nerve cells. In the central nervous system the nerve cells are supported by a delicate and very fragile tissue called *neuroglia* (literally, nerve glue). The brain and spinal cord are made up of two distinct types of this soft nervous tissue called *gray matter* and *white matter* which differ greatly in histologic structure.

In contrast to the nervous tissue of the central nervous system the nerves of the peripheral nervous system are tough. This firm quality is derived from the considerable amount of connective tissue which covers and supports the bundles of nerve fibers. A microscopic examination of a cross section of a nerve shows it to be circular in shape and covered by a connective tissue wrapping, or *sheath*. Inside this sheath are several bundles of *nerve fibers*, each bundle being surrounded by another connective tissue sheath. Each nerve fiber inside the bundles is encased in its individual connective tissue sheath, and often between this sheath and the individual fiber is a layer of substance of a fatty nature called a *myelin sheath*. Each nerve fiber in this nerve is actually a long, thin, stretched-out part of the cytoplasm of a neuron. The body of the neuron, which contains the nucleus, lies deep in the body of the individual.

Nerve cells do not multiply with the growth of the human body. A person is born with all the neurons he will ever possess. However, if a fiber in the peripheral nervous system is cut, repair may eventually take place. The end of the fiber which has been cut off from the body of the neuron will degenerate, and the end of the fiber still attached to the neuron may after a time grow out to the length of the original fiber. In the central nervous system, on the other hand, damage is permanent. There is no regeneration following damage to the brain or spinal cord.

MUSCLE TISSUE

Muscle tissue is composed of muscle cells which are supported by connective tissue. Muscle cells are in all cases much longer than they are wide, and for this reason an individual muscle cell is called a muscle fiber. Muscle fibers have to a greater degree than other cells the property of contraction.

Microscopic examination of muscle tissue from various parts of the body shows a difference in the appearance of the cytoplasm of muscle fibers. In muscle tissue from some areas, for example from the intestine, the cytoplasm of the muscle fibers appears relatively clear. In muscle tissue from other areas, such as from the arm or the heart, the cytoplasm of the muscle fibers has conspicuous cross striations. This difference in the appearance of the cytoplasm of different muscle fibers led histologists to classify muscle tissue as *smooth muscle tissue* (where the cytoplasm of the fibers is not cross striated), and *striated muscle tissue* (where the cytoplasm of the fibers is cross striated). (See Figures 13, *E* and 13, *F*.)

This division of muscle tissue into two types was not quite adequate, however. Smooth muscle is *involuntary muscle*—that is, the contraction of its fibers is not under the control of the will of the individual. For instance, the peristaltic movements of the intestine, which contains smooth muscle in its walls, are not willfully controlled. On the other hand, striated muscle is for the most part *voluntary muscle* because the contractions of the muscle fibers may be consciously controlled by the individual. One moves an arm or a leg as one wishes. However, there is an exception. The fibers of heart muscle, although striated like the fibers of the muscles of the arm, are not consciously controlled by the individual. Therefore cardiac muscle has been described as belonging to a class by itself and is called *striated involuntary muscle* in contrast to skeletal muscle which is referred to as *striated voluntary muscle*.

Thus we arrive at a classification for muscle tissue consisting of three catagories: *smooth muscle, striated voluntary muscle,* and *striated involuntary muscle.*

Smooth muscle tissue is found in such places as in the walls of the intestines, in the walls of blood vessels (Fig. 15), and at the roots of hairs where its contraction produces an erection of the hair. The individual muscle fibers (cells) of smooth muscle tissue are shaped somewhat like a cigar and have a centrally located nucleus (Fig. 13, *E*). In length they may vary from 1/1000 mm. in the small blood vessels to $\frac{1}{2}$ mm. in the pregnant uterus. The fibers are supported by associated connective tissue.

Striated voluntary muscle is known also as *skeletal muscle.* As well as the obvious inclusion in this class of such muscles as those which move the arms and legs, skeletal muscles also include those in and about the oral cavity: muscles of the tongue, of the lips and cheeks, of the soft palate. The muscle fibers of skeletal muscle differ in a number of ways from those

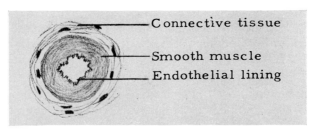

FIGURE 15.—Diagram of a cross section of a blood vessel. (Low power magnification.)

of smooth muscle. Most conspicuous of course is the difference in the appearance of the cytoplasm, which shows microscopic cross striations (Fig. 13, *F*). Also, the nuclei in skeletal muscle fibers are pushed to one side of the fibers instead of lying in the center, and there is more than one nucleus in a fiber. Skeletal muscle fibers are relatively long, varying from 1 to 40 mm., and they are supported by connective tissue which not only covers individual fibers, but binds the fibers into bundles. This supporting connective tissue is well supplied with blood vessels and nerves.

Striated involuntary muscle is confined to the heart and is known also as *cardiac muscle.* In microscopic appearance it resembles skeletal muscle in that the cytoplasm of the muscle fibers has microscopic cross striations. Its appearance differs from that of skeletal muscle in the arrangement of the fibers. Whereas skeletal muscle fibers exist as individual fibers with several nuclei, cardiac muscle fibers branch and come together so that they form a sort of network which comprises the heart muscle. This network is supported by surrounding connective tissue which contains nerves and a rich supply of blood vessels.

Muscles are the organs responsible for both the voluntary and the involuntary movement of all of the various parts of the body. They act in response to impulses received from the nervous system. They are surrounded by, supported by, and nourished by the different kinds of connective tissue: the fibrous, areolar, and adipose; the bone and cartilage; and the blood.

ORAL HISTOLOGY

Of particular importance in Dentistry are the tissues of the oral cavity. The entire practice of Dentistry and Dental Hygiene is based on a knowledge of the structure, arrangement, and reactions of oral tissues. Instructions given to a patient by the dentist and the dental hygienist concerning the correct method of brushing the teeth are based on a knowledge of oral histology. A dentist prepares a tooth for a filling with careful attention to the nature and arrangement of the tissues comprising the tooth; and he constructs an artificial denture with regard for the structure of the tissues of the palate, of the alveolar ridge, and of the oral vestibule. The pathosis which occurs in the tissues around a tooth when calculus is present can be understood only in the light of a knowledge of tissue structure and tissue reaction; and the tissue repair which follows removal of the calculus is explainable in the same terms. Other diseases of the soft tissues of the mouth are recognized and treated only as normal tissue structure is known. The nearly universal disease of the hard tooth tissues, dental caries, must be described in terms of the microscopic structure of the calcified tissues of a tooth.

Oral histology is the study of the tissues of the oral cavity: the tissues lining the mouth and the tissues beneath the lining, the tissues of the tongue, the periodontium, the tooth, and the tissues from which a tooth develops. This text will include also a study of the process of tooth development.

LOCATION OF ORAL TISSUES

The relative locations of some of the oral tissues may be seen in the diagram of a section through a human mandible in the region of the first premolar tooth (Fig. 55). The *tooth* is attached by fibers of the *periodontal ligament* to the *lamina dura* which comprises the tooth socket. The outside surface of the mandible consists of *cortical bone* inside of which is *cancellous bone* and bone marrow. The lining of the inside of the cheek, the gingiva, and the covering of the *tongue* are mucous membrane. Under the tongue are located the *salivary glands* and several *muscles*.

TISSUES OF A TOOTH

The tissues which make up a tooth are the enamel, the dentin, the cementum, and the pulp. Figures 16, 17, 18 and 19 are diagrams of teeth which have been cut approximately through the middle in a faciolingual direction. *Tooth enamel* comprises the surface of the crown of the tooth and *cementum* comprises the surface of the tooth root. *Dentin*, which lies beneath the enamel of the crown and beneath the cementum of the root, makes up the bulk of the hard tissue of the tooth. The *tooth pulp* is the only noncalcified tissue of the tooth. It occupies the *pulp chamber* in the crown of the tooth and continues through the *root canals* to its union with the periodontal ligament at the *apical foramen*.

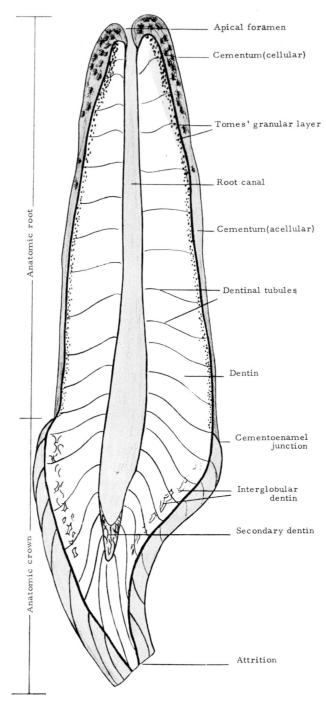

FIGURE 16.—Diagrammatic drawing of a longitudinal faciolingual section of a maxillary incisor tooth. The cementum lacunæ in this and in the following diagrams of tooth sections are somewhat exaggerated in size. For identification of unlabelled structures see Figures 17, 18 and 19.

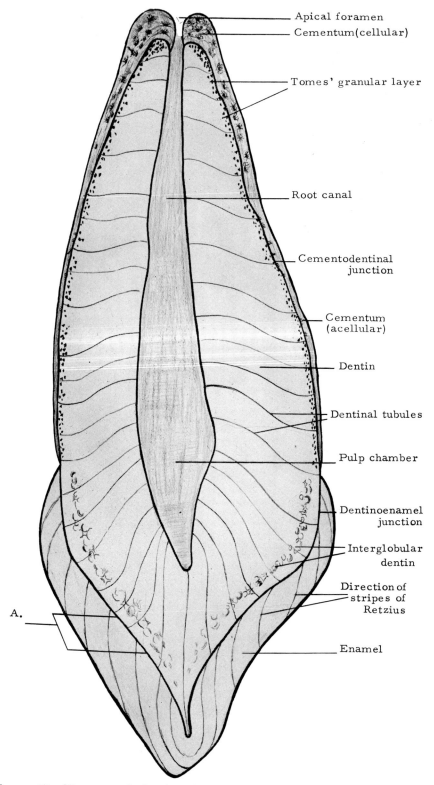

Apical foramen

Cementum(cellular)

Tomes' granular layer

Root canal

Cementodentinal
junction

Cementum
(acellular)

Dentin

Dentinal tubules

Pulp chamber

Dentinoenamel
junction

Interglobular
dentin

Direction of
stripes of
Retzius

Enamel

A.

FIGURE 17.—Diagrammatic drawing of a longitudinal faciolingual section of a maxillary canine tooth. The area marked *A* indicates a location in the enamel similar to that shown in Figure 27.

(41)

The line of union between the dentin and the enamel is the *dentino-enamel junction*. The line of union between the dentin and the cementum is the *dentinocemental junction*. The line of union between the cementum and the enamel is the *cementoenamel junction*. These are frequent points of reference in descriptions of a tooth.

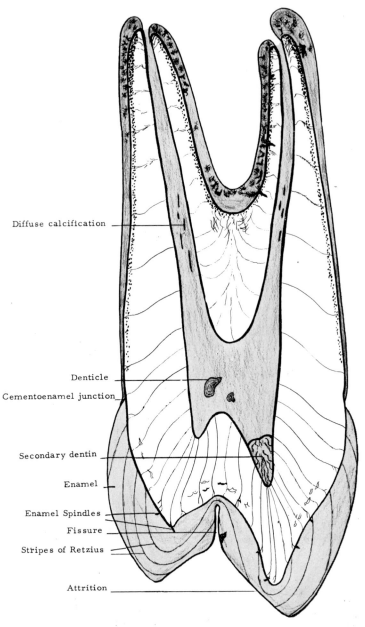

Diffuse calcification

Denticle

Cementoenamel junction

Secondary dentin

Enamel

Enamel Spindles

Fissure

Stripes of Retzius

Attrition

FIGURE 18.—Diagrammatic drawing of a longitudinal faciolingual section of a maxillary first premolar tooth. See Figure 1 for a photograph of a similar tooth and compare the structures indicated in the diagrammatic drawing with the same structures seen in the photograph of the actual tooth section.

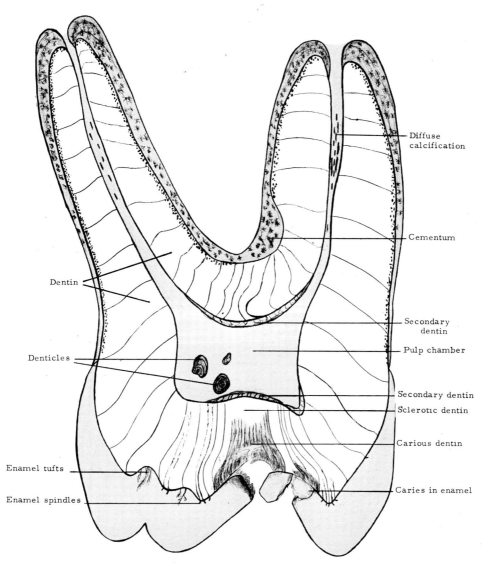

Diffuse
calcification

Cementum

Dentin

Secondary
dentin

Pulp chamber

Denticles

Secondary dentin

Sclerotic dentin

Carious dentin

Enamel tufts

Enamel spindles

Caries in enamel

FIGURE 19.—Diagrammatic drawing of a longitudinal faciolingual section of a maxillary first molar tooth. Dental caries has destroyed the enamel in the area around a developmental groove on the occlusal surface. The caries has spread horizontally at the dentinoenamel junction, with a resultant undermining of enamel. Caries has spread pulpward in the dentinal tubules to about $\frac{2}{3}$ the thickness of the dentin. The dentin close to the pulp is sclerotic dentin: the tubules are filled with mineral salts. On the pulpal wall beneath the carious lesion a small amount of secondary dentin has formed. The secondary dentin on the floor of the pulp chamber (next to the root) was not caused by caries; secondary dentin in this location is not unusual. (See Figure 36).

3

Tooth Enamel

LOCATION

Tooth enamel makes up the outside layer of the anatomic crown of a tooth (Figs. 1 and 16).

COMPOSITION

Enamel is composed of both inorganic (mineral) and organic substances. Mature human enamel is about 96 per cent inorganic. The remaining 4 per cent of its substance is an organic matrix (framework) and water. Enamel is the hardest tissue of the body, its mineral content far exceeding the mineral content of dentin (70 per cent), of cementum (50 per cent), or of bone (50 per cent).

MACROSCOPIC STRUCTURE OF ENAMEL

Examine the teeth of several persons who maintain reasonably good oral hygiene. The crown surfaces are composed of hard, shiny enamel. In young individuals who are free from dental caries, no other tooth tissues are exposed in the oral cavity. On some of the teeth of older individuals, due to a normal aging process, the gingiva may have receded to such an extent that cementum is visible. In persons of any age whose teeth have unrepaired carious lesions, dentin will be exposed in the areas where the disease has destroyed the enamel.

On the labial surfaces of the maxillary central incisors of a young person you usually see a number of fine horizontal lines on the enamel. In the cervical part of the crown these lines are close together; incisally on the crown they are farther apart (Fig. 20). These lines are called *perikymata*. Their presence is not confined to the maxillary central incisors, but they are easier to see here than on less accessible surfaces. In older persons perikymata usually are not visible.

Examination of the teeth of persons of different ages will show that generally in older persons the enamel appears darker in color than in younger persons. The reason for this darkening is not clearly understood.

Despite its hardness tooth enamel is subject to attrition—that is, wearing off under the friction of use. Examine the teeth of several middle-aged persons. Probably you will find the enamel of the molar cusps worn so that the cusp tips are nearly flat. Sometimes the enamel is entirely worn off of the cusp tips and the exposed dentin is seen as dark spots. In the anterior teeth the incisal edges of the central and lateral incisors may be sufficiently worn so that dentin is seen as a fine dark line extending mesiodistally on the incisal edge. These conditions of attrition in older individuals are not abnormal but are merely a natural aging process. Accompanying changes in the dentin beneath the worn enamel protect the tooth pulp from damage (Chapter 4, sclerotic and secondary dentin).

Examine the newly emerged incisor teeth of a six- or seven-year-old child. There are probably three prominences, or scallops, along the incisal edge. These prominences are called *mamelons* They are developmental structures, but are of no clinical importance. Usually they are worn off early in the life of the tooth. (Figs. 35 and 50.)

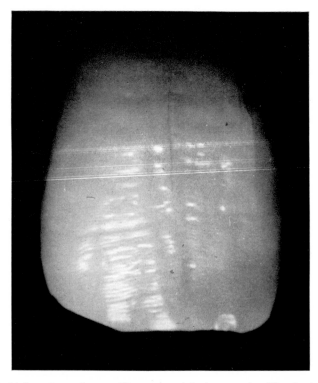

FIGURE 20.—Labial surface of a maxillary central incisor tooth. The horizontal lines are perikymata.

In an adult mouth look carefully at the posterior teeth and observe the developmental grooves that mark the occlusal surfaces. Developmental grooves will also be found on the buccal surfaces of maxillary and mandibular molars, on the lingual surfaces of maxillary molars, and sometimes on the lingual surfaces of maxillary incisors. The structure of these developmental grooves varies: In some teeth they are shallow and smooth (Figs. 30 and 31). In other teeth the grooves have deep fissures along the length of their base (Figs. 1, 23, 32, 33, 34). On occlusal surfaces the grooves and fissures may end in deep pits in the mesial and distal triangular fossæ or in the central fossa. On the buccal and lingual surfaces the grooves may have a deep pit at their cervical end. It will be impossible to see, in examining the mouth, how deep such fissures and pits are; and usually it will be impossible to insert even the smallest dental instrument or toothbrush bristle into them (Figs. 1 and 23). The pit or fissure does not extend into the dentin: it always ends in the enamel. And there is always a little enamel, however thin, at the base of the pit or fissure (Figs. 23, 32, 33, 34). Enamel structure in fissures is studied, of course, not by looking in the mouth, but by examination of ground sections of extracted teeth.

In thickness the enamel varies in different parts of the tooth crown. At its thickest parts it may be 2 or 2.5 mm. thick, while at the cervical line it thins to a knife edge. Examine Figures 16, 17, 18, 19 and 21 for an idea of the relative thickness of the enamel in different locations.

Enveloping the entire crown of a newly erupted tooth and adhering firmly to its surface is an organic covering called the *enamel cuticle* (sometimes called *secondary enamel cuticle*). This covering is not visible in clinical examinations, but it may be demonstrated in the laboratory by immersing an extracted young tooth in a dish of acid and allowing it to stand undisturbed until the mineral substance of the enamel is dissolved away. When the enamel is gone there remains a nearly transparent membrane, somewhat resembling a cellophane bag, suspended in the solution in the position where the surface of the enamel has previously been. This thin covering is the enamel cuticle, and because it is organic it was not dissolved by the acid. It is very fragile and will be washed away as soon as the dish in which the tooth stands is slightly shaken. In the mouth this noncalcified cuticle is probably soon worn off of areas which occlude with opposing teeth, such as the tips of the molar cusps. It may be retained for some time in more protected areas.

MICROSCOPIC STRUCTURE OF ENAMEL

Enamel can be studied by various methods. You can examine thin ground sections of extracted teeth and see in their natural relationship the organic and inorganic substances which comprise enamel. Or the organic portion, the matrix, which is in the form of a delicate framework, can be examined separately by using special careful techniques to dissolve away the mineral substances. In recent years new techniques have enabled the histologist to study enamel and other tooth tissues with the electron microscope at magnifications of the order of $5,000 \times$ to $40,000 \times$ and more.

Tooth enamel is made up of minute *rods* which extend from the dentino-enamel junction to the outer surface of the enamel. They are arranged roughly perpendicular to the dentinoenamel junction (Fig. 21). Usually the rods are not perfectly straight; in some parts of the tooth, particularly in the occlusal areas, they have multiple curvatures. It has been estimated that a human maxillary central incisor contains 8,586,000 enamel rods, and that a maxillary first molar contains 12,297,000 rods. The average diameter of a rod is about 4 microns (approximately 4/25,000 inch). Each enamel rod is composed of a series of small units which fit together in a row somewhat like a string of beads (Figs. 22 and 38). This segmented construction is a result of the manner of formation of the enamel rods (Chapter 11).

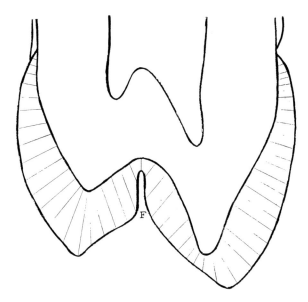

FIGURE 21.—Diagrammatic drawing of a longitudinal faciolingual section of the crown of a maxillary first premolar tooth. The lines in the enamel illustrate the general direction of the enamel rods. Notice the narrowness of the fissure (F) and the thinness of the enamel at the bottom of the fissure. Notice also the radiating pattern of the enamel rods in the fissure.

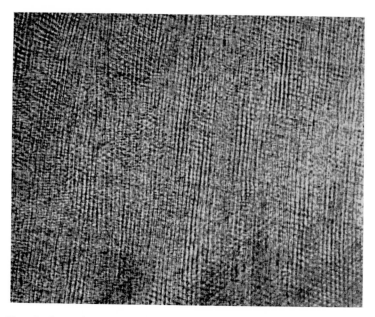

FIGURE 22.—A photomicrograph (high power) of a ground section of human enamel. In this picture the rods are in a vertical position, and in this area they are nearly straight. The cross striations in the rods are discernible.

Each enamel rod is encased in a *rod sheath*, and the sheathed rods are cemented together by an *interrod substance*. Of these three structures, the rods are the most highly calcified, the cementing substance is slightly less calcified than the rods, and the rod sheaths are slightly less calcified than the cementing substance. However, all three structures are extremely hard. The organic substance which they contain has been shown by the electron microscope to be in the form of a fine fibrillar latticework. This latticework, or framework, of the rods, rod sheaths, and interrod substance is the *organic matrix* of the enamel. In suitable preparations this matrix may be examined with an ordinary microscope, but the fibrils of which it is composed are so minute that its fibrillar character can be seen only by the use of the electron microscope.

The entire organic substance of enamel comprises only about 4 per cent of its composition. The other 96 per cent of enamel is mineral substance which exists in the form of tightly packed *submicroscopic crystals*. These

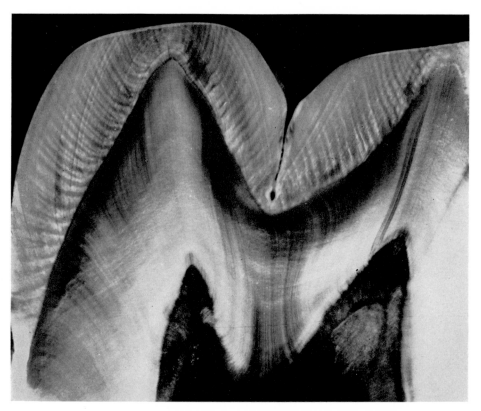

FIGURE 23.—Ground section cut buccolingually through a mandibular molar tooth. In the enamel the dark and light bands of Hunter-Schreger extend from the dentinoenamel junction to the enamel surface nearly perpendicular to the dentinoenamel junction. The stripes of Retzius are faintly visible, starting at the dentinoenamel junction and extending outward and occlusally, reaching the enamel surface excepting near the cusp tip (See Fig. 18). In this tooth there is some attrition on the cusp tips. Secondary dentin (Chapter 4) is seen in the pulp horns. Considering the magnification of this picture, it is clear that the fissure is too narrow to permit the insertion of any dental instrument. The enamel at the base of the fissure is thin. It shows no sign of caries.

crystals fill the loose organic matrix. Their size is appreciated when we learn that they are measured in terms of millionths of a millimeter.

Microscopic examination of a thin ground tooth section shows other structures in enamel: *bands of Hunter-Schreger, stripes of Retzius, enamel lamellæ, enamel tufts,* and *enamel spindles.* Some of these structures are of no known clinical importance, while others are of great importance.

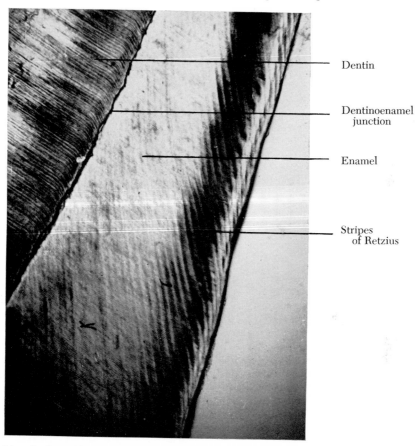

Dentin

Dentinoenamel
junction

Enamel

Stripes
of Retzius

FIGURE 24.—A photomicrograph of a small area of tooth crown cut longitudinally. Stripes of Retzius in the enamel are clearly visible. The direction of the dentinal tubules can also be seen. (Low power magnification.)

Bands of Hunter-Schreger are seen when a longitudinal ground section of a tooth crown is examined by reflected light under the low power of the microscope (Fig. 23). They are alternating broad light and dark bands which extend perpendicularly from the dentinoenamel junction to the tooth surface. Their manifestation is due to the curvature of the enamel rods.

The *stripes of Retzius* are a different kind of bands, or lines, in the enamel. In longitudinal ground sections of the tooth crown they are seen under the low power of the microscope as narrow brownish lines extending diagonally outward from the dentinoenamel junction toward the occlusal, or incisal, part of the crown (Figs. 17, 18, 23, and 24). These structures are formed

4

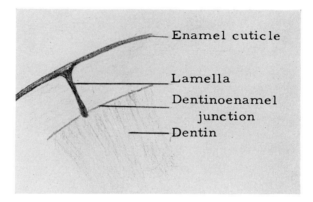

FIGURE 25.—Schematic diagram of a small area of a cross section of a tooth crown in the region of an enamel lamella.

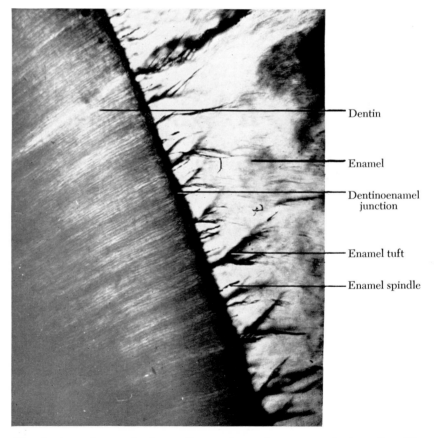

FIGURE 26.—A photomicrograph of a small area of a tooth crown cut horizontally. The enamel tufts are clearly visible. Among the tufts, in some places, are seen the much smaller enamel spindles. (As seen under low power magnification.)

during the development of the enamel matrix as a result of the layer-upon-layer pattern of enamel matrix formation. They are due to variations in structure and calcification along the lines corresponding to the formation pattern. On most of the crown the stripes of Retzius end on the crown surface, and their termination on the surface sometimes is marked by a series of shallow depressions. The ridges between the depressions are called the *perikymata*. Near the incisal or occlusal part of the crown the stripes of Retzius do not reach the enamel surface and therefore there are no perikymata at the incisal edge or cusp tips (Fig. 18). Perikymata often may be seen in clinical examination. To the dental hygienist the stripes of Retzius are of interest chiefly because of their association with the perikymata. (Fig. 20).

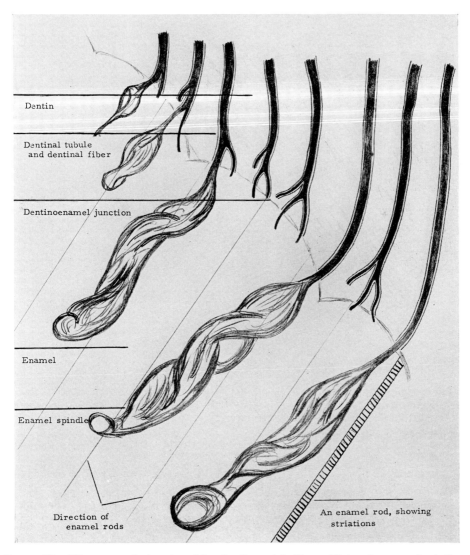

FIGURE 27.—Diagrammatic drawing of details of area A in Figure 17 showing enamel spindles. (Very high power magnification.)

Enamel lamellæ (literally the word means *little layers*) have been described as faults in enamel matrix formation and as cracks in the enamel due to injury. Certainly they are microscopic separations in the enamel which extend inward from the enamel surface for varying distances and which are filled with organic material (Fig. 25). Lamellæ may sometimes be seen by using the low power of the microscope on a ground section of tooth crown.

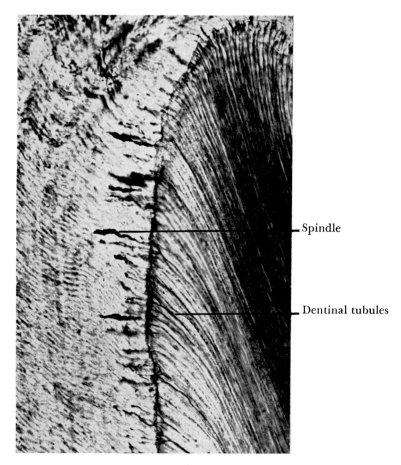

Spindle

Dentinal tubules

FIGURE 28.—A ground section of a tooth crown near cusp tip. Enamel is on left of the picture, dentin on right. Many enamel spindles are protruding from the dentinoenamel junction. Notice that the direction of the spindles is different from the direction of the rods of the enamel (Medium power magnification.)

Enamel tufts also are visible in ground tooth sections. Microscopically they look like small brushes which are attached to the dentinoenamel junction and which extend outward in the enamel to perhaps as much as a fifth of the distance to the surface (Figs. 19 and 26). Histologically they are hypocalcified, or uncalcified, inner ends of some groups of enamel rods, with their rod sheaths and surrounding interrod substance.

Enamel spindles are ends of dentinal fibers which project from the dentin across the dentinoenamel junction into the enamel (Figs. 18, 26, 27, 28, 29). These structures will be understood when you study the structure of dentin.

The *dentinoenamel junction* in many teeth is not a straight line, but rather a scalloped line in which small curved projections of enamel fit into small concavities of the dentin (Fig. 38).

Enamel contains no cells; it is a product of special enamel-forming cells. It has no circulation in the form of blood vessels or other structures, but that it is permeable to some substances has been demonstrated in studies using dyes and solutions of radioactive substances. Any clinical significance of this permeability is not at present understood.

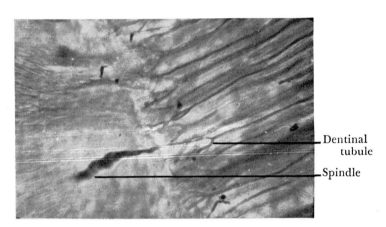

FIGURE 29.—Photomicrograph of an enamel spindle as seen with the oil immersion objective of the microscope. Enamel is at left, dentin is at right of the picture. It is possible to see that the spindle was a continuation of the dentinal fiber. Notice the branching of the dentinal tubules at the dentinoenamel junction (Chapter 4).

PERMANENCE OF ENAMEL STRUCTURE

Once tooth enamel is formed the calcification is never decreased by any physiological process within the tooth. All present evidence indicates that mineral substance is not withdrawn from enamel once it has been deposited there. The notion that pregnancy produces a withdrawal of calcium from the teeth of the mother is not supported by factual evidence.

Enamel has no possibility of anatomic self-repair following damage by injury or by caries. In the study of tooth eruption it will be seen that the cells which form the enamel in the developing tooth are lost when the tooth emerges into the mouth, making subsequent enamel formation impossible.

CLINICAL IMPORTANCE OF THE STRUCTURE OF ENAMEL

The structure of enamel is important clinically for several reasons: its hardness makes it resistant to the friction of ordinary use; the curvatures of the enamel rods probably increase the strength of the enamel; the presence of pits and fissures influences the occurrence of dental caries; and the arrangement of the enamel rods and the presence of areas of less mineralization influence the pattern and speed of progress of dental caries.

Let us consider how the structure of enamel may affect the clinical condition of an individual.

The high mineral content of enamel makes it a very hard substance which is resistant to, but no proof against, attrition (Figs. 16, 23, 33, and 63). On the incisal edges of anterior teeth and on the cusp tips of posterior teeth, where the teeth of opposing arches meet forcefully in occlusion, attrition may be sufficient to expose the underlying dentin.

The *perikymata* which usually mark the enamel on all surfaces of all teeth are of no clinical importance.

The *bands of Hunter-Schreger* are visible in ground sections of teeth because of the curvatures in the enamel rods. These curvatures probably make the enamel stronger by reducing the chances of cleavage (splitting) of the enamel along the rod length.

Enamel lamellæ are believed by some investigators to be areas which are particularly susceptible to dental caries. Other investigators disagree with this idea.

The *stripes of Retzius*, being areas of slightly more organic material, tend to facilitate the lateral spread of caries along the line of each stripe. However, this lateral spread is considerably less pronounced than the lateral spread of caries which occurs along the dentinoenamel junction in areas of tufts and spindles.

Enamel tufts and *enamel spindles* near the dentinoenamel junction, the presence of *pits* and *fissures* on the occlusal, buccal, and lingual surfaces of teeth, and the pattern of arrangement of the enamel rods are of great importance clinically because of their determinate influence on the occurrence and pattern of dental caries.

To explain the role that these structures play in the caries process it is necessary to review the nature of dental caries. Dental caries is a disease of the hard tissues of the teeth in which the mineral substance of the tooth is dissolved by acid and the then exposed organic substance is destroyed by proteolysis. The acid is produced by the kinds of oral bacteria which, in the process of their metabolism, convert carbohydrates, especially sugars, into acids. Caries-susceptible individuals have in their saliva and in their dental plaques large numbers of these acidogenic (acid-producing) bacteria.

The bacteria which cause the damage are the ones which are located in the dental plaques. A *dental plaque* is a dense accumulation of microorganisms which adheres firmly to the surface of a tooth. In mouths kept ordinarily clean, plaques are found chiefly in protected areas—around contact areas, and in pits and fissures. (Fig. 30.)

A known sequence of events follows the oral intake of sugar by a caries-susceptible person: Food taken into the mouth is retained in the area of the plaque; the acidogenic bacteria of the plaque reduce the sugars to acids; the acids in the plaque are in contact with the enamel surface to which the plaque is attached; and since tooth enamel is soluble in acid, the enamel beneath the plaque is slightly dissolved. This is the beginning of a caries lesion. Repeated eating of sugar results in repeated periods of enamel dissolution.

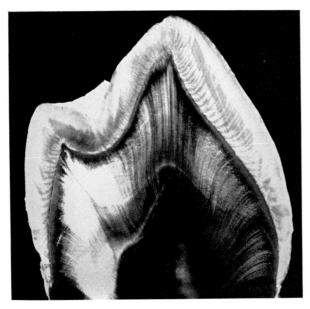

FIGURE 30.—Ground section cut buccolingually through a mandibular first premolar tooth. The developmental groove on the occlusal surface of the tooth is not deep, and there is no fissure at its base. No caries is present in this groove. A plaque is retained in the groove. If the plaque is mineralized, it is called calculus.

Notice the direction of the dentinal tubules which extend from the dentinoenamel junction to the pulp chamber (Chapter 4). (Low power magnification.)

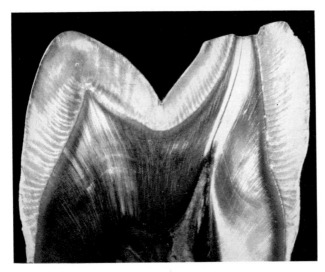

FIGURE 31.—Ground section of a molar tooth. The developmental groove on the occlusal surface does not have a fissure at its base. No dental caries is present in the groove. Notice the direction of the dentinal tubules. The pulp horn extends far into the cusp (Chapter 5).

Now, how does the structure of enamel influence the occurrence and the pattern of dental caries?

First, let us consider the effect of *fissures* and *pits* on the occurrence and pattern of dental caries. While teeth which do not have fissures at the base of their developmental grooves (Figs. 30 and 31) may, and sometimes do, have caries in these shallow grooves, teeth which do have fissures at the base of their developmental grooves have, in the depths of these narrow depressions, an ideal environment for the development of dental caries. The fissures and pits may be so narrow and so deep that even the smallest instrument cannot be inserted to the bottom (Figs. 23, 32, 33, 34, 35); but they are not too small to permit the entrance of bacteria and of foods. A

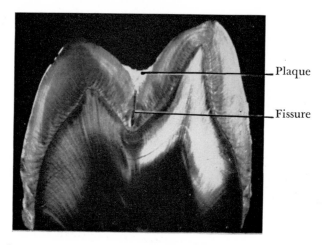

Plaque

Fissure

FIGURE 32.—Ground section through a maxillary first premolar tooth cut buccolingually. The central developmental groove has a deep fissure at its base. The thin enamel at the bottom of the fissure seems to be intact, but the appearance of the dentin immediately beneath it suggests that caries was present in the fissure at one side or the other of the section here seen, and that the lesion had spread near the dentinoenamel junction, undermining the sound surface enamel. A dense plaque is present in the *groove*, but in this particular area it seems not to be dense enough within the *fissure* to be visible in the photomicrograph.

fissure or a pit is a sheltered, warm, moist, richly-provided incubator, and a dental plaque can be expected to form here (Figs. 32 and 33). In a caries-susceptible person acid is produced by acidogenic bacteria in the plaque and this acid damages the enamel walls of the fissure. This is the start of fissure caries.

In fissure caries, or in caries occurring around contact areas, or in caries in any other location on the tooth crown, the pattern of arrangement of the enamel rods in the affected area determines the direction of penetration of the lesion. This is true because caries progresses more rapidly in areas where there is less mineral substance to be dissolved away—that is, in areas of lower mineralization; and the rod sheaths and interrod substance are less mineralized than the rods. In microscopic study of sections of carious enamel it can be seen that the lesion penetrates along the direction of the rod length.

On the smooth facial, lingual, and proximal surfaces of a tooth the enamel rods lie nearly perpendicular to the straight or broadly convex dentinoenamel junction (Fig. 21), even though they show characteristic curvatures (seen in the bands of Hunter-Schreger). Therefore, a lesion occurring around a contact area, for instance, penetrates more or less in a straight line toward the dentinoenamel junction.

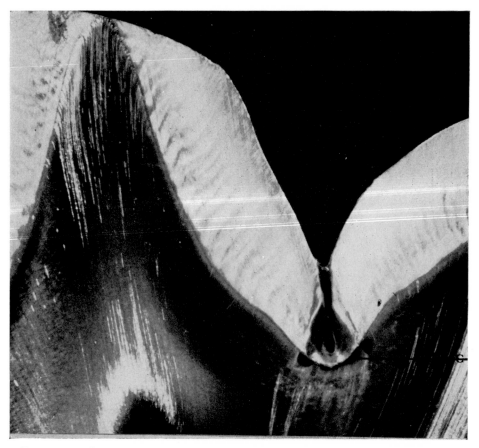

FIGURE 33.—Ground section of a molar tooth. The fissure in the occlusal developmental groove clearly is affected by dental caries. Notice the radiating pattern of the lesion in the enamel near the bottom of the fissure. This is due to the fanning out of the enamel rods. (See Figure 21.) The dentin beneath the bottom of the fissure is destroyed near the dentinoenamel junction (C), leaving the enamel unsupported. There is little evidence of sclerosis of the dentin beneath this lesion. The bacteria here have probably penetrated well into the dentinal tubules (Chapter 4). The plaque is indistinctly seen in this ground section. Often plaques are destroyed in the process of grinding the section. Notice attrition on the cusp tip.

In the base of fissures the enamel rods still lie nearly perpendicular to the dentinoenamel junction, but the sharp concavity of the junction in this location results in a radial pattern—a fanning out—of the rods (Fig. 21). The caries lesion starting at the base of the fissure and penetrating in the direction of the rod length, radiates as it deepens (Fig. 33). The resulting clinical picture may be only a small carious area visible in a developmental groove; but at the dentinoenamel junction, invisible without x-ray pictures, the broadening of the lesion has left the surface enamel unsupported (Fig. 36).

We may therefore conclude that a fissure offers an ideal site for the formation of a dental plaque; and if the individual is caries-susceptible, caries will probably develop in the fissure, and the radiating arrangement of the enamel rods in the area will cause a subsurface spreading of the lesion.

Now let us consider the effect of the presence of *enamel tufts* and *enamel spindles* on the pattern of a caries lesion. Dental caries always begins on

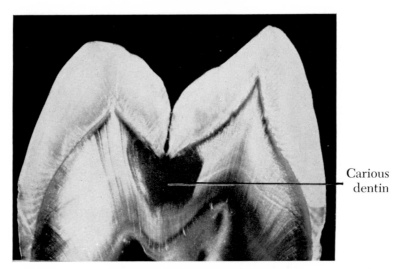

Carious
dentin

FIGURE 34.—Ground section of a molar tooth. In this tooth the caries started in the enamel at the bottom of the fissure and spread along the dentinoenamel junction. In this area the lesion has visibly penetrated the dentin, and the effect of caries is seen in the dentin over a broad area at the dentinoenamel junction and pulpward. The dark region in the dentin beneath the fissure, broad near the dentinoenamel junction and more narrow nearer the pulp, is carious dentin. (See Chapter 4) Caries will spread downward, destroying the unaffected dentin beneath it and around it. Destruction of dentin will leave the superficial enamel unsupported.

the outside surface of a tooth, never, so far as we know, on the inside. But as the surface enamel beneath a plaque is destroyed by caries, the lesion deepens and eventually reaches the area of tufts and spindles near the dentinoenamel junction. As we have seen, caries spreads more rapidly in areas of low mineralization than in areas of high mineralization, and tufts and spindles are unmineralized, or hypomineralized, structures. Therefore, there is a horizontal spread of the lesion in the enamel near the dentinoenamel junction. The enamel which is superficial to the deep spreading lesion often shows no injury except at the point of initial damage under the plaque; but for an extended area around this point of entry, the intact superficial enamel is undermined by caries and is therefore unsupported (Fig. 36).

With these several structural characteristics of enamel tending to produce a spread of caries beneath the enamel surface, it is easy to see how one day an individual may bite on such an area and part of the surface of a seemingly (to the patient) good tooth will cave in. An understanding of the subsurface spread of dental caries* motivates the dental hygienist to instruct patients of the importance of regular dental examinations and of the necessity for prompt attention to even seemingly small cavities.

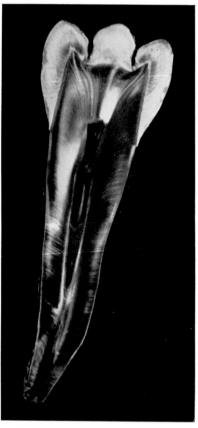

FIGURE 35.—Ground section of a mandibular incisor tooth cut mesiodistally. The intact tooth had mamelons that appeared unusually pronounced. The ground section shows deep pits in the depressions between the mamelons, with a very thin layer of enamel at the base of the pits. In making ground sections of a number of teeth that had unusually pronounced mamelons, it was found that such pits were generally present. Notice the curvature of the dentinal tubules in the tooth crown. In the root the tubules are nearly straight and are directed slightly apically from the cementodentinal junction.

*A word about the term *dental caries: Caries* is the correct form of the word. You may say that a person has caries; or that he has a carious tooth; or that he has a cavity in a tooth. Or you may say that caries *is* (singular verb) present in a mouth. But you never say a person has "a carie"— any more than you say a person has a *measle* or a *mump*.

4

Dentin

LOCATION

Dentin is located in both the crown and the root of a tooth, making up the bulk of the tooth. In an intact tooth the dentin is not visible because in the crown it is covered by enamel and in the root it is covered by cementum (Figs. 19 and 36).

COMPOSTION

Dentin is a calcified tissue, and like all calcified tissues of the body it is composed of both *organic* and *inorganic* (mineral) substances. Although not nearly so hard as tooth enamel, dentin is harder than bone. Mature dentin is about 70 per cent inorganic substance and about 30 per cent organic material and water. (Compare these figures with those given for enamel in Chapter 3.)

STRUCTURE OF DENTIN

Dentin is made up of a calcified *matrix* which is perforated by *dentinal tubules*. The dentinal tubules contain *dentinal fibers*.

The dentin matrix is an organic framework composed of very small *fibrils* surrounded and held together by a structureless *cementing substance*. During the development of dentin, the organic matrix is formed first and then minerals in solution are deposited in its cementing substance. These minerals then crystalize out of solution and the crystals form on and around the minute fibrils. Thus the organic matrix of the dentin becomes hardened and the dentin is a calcified tissue. The mineral substance of dentin is similar to the mineral substances of enamel, cementum, and bone.

Dentin is perforated by innumerable holes called *dentinal tubules* which contain *dentinal fibers* (not to be confused with the *fibrils* of the dentin matrix). The dentinal tubules lie close together and extend from the tooth pulp to the dentinoenamel junction in the crown of the tooth and to the dentinocemental junction in the root (Figs. 1, 16, 23). At their outer ends the dentinal tubules are divided into a number of branches (Figs. 28 and 29). Much smaller branches connecting adjacent dentinal tubules are often found along the length of the tubules. In diameter the dentinal tubules measure about 4 microns (4/25,000 inch) at the pulpal ends and somewhat less at the outer ends. In the cusp tips in the tooth crown (Fig. 34) and in the apical half of the root (Figs. 35 and 36) the dentinal tubules are nearly straight and are arranged nearly perpendicular to the dentinoenamel or dentinocemental junction. In the facial, lingual,

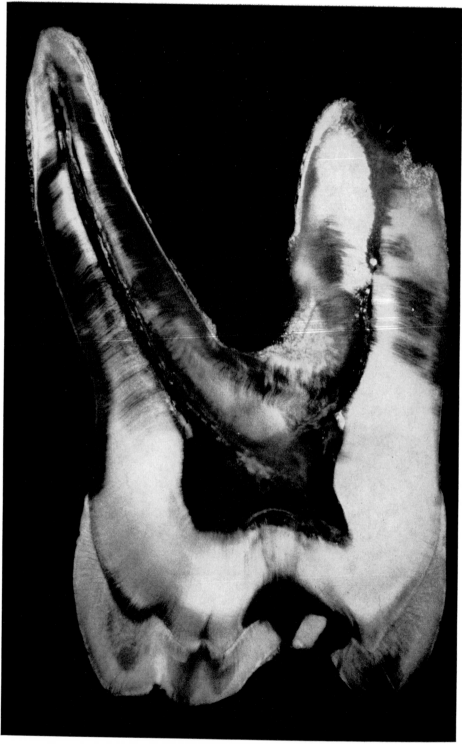

FIGURE 36.—A photomicrograph of a ground section cut faciolingually through a maxillary first molar tooth. This tooth is shown diagrammatically in Figure 19. (Very low power magnification.)

mesial, and distal areas of the crown (Figs. 30 and 35) and in the cervical portion of the roots (Fig. 36) the dentinal tubules are S-shaped. The outer ends of the S-shaped tubules are always occlusal to the pulpal ends of the tubules.

A *dentinal fiber* (also called a *Tomes' fiber*) occupies each dentinal tubule

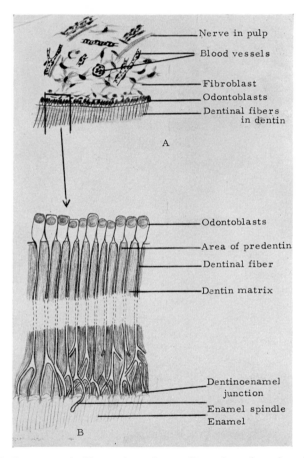

FIGURE 37.—A diagrammatic illustration of a small portion of tooth pulp showing the structure of the pulp and the relation of the odontoblast cells of the pulp to the dentin and the enamel. *A.* Tooth pulp as seen under high power magnification. *B.* Diagrammatic illustration of the small enclosed area shown in *A.* The odontoblast cells of the pulp have cytoplasmic processes, the dentinal fibers, which extend in the dentinal tubules to the dentinoenamel junction. The fibers are branched at their peripheral ends. The portion of the odontoblast process that crosses the dentinoenamel junction into the enamel is an enamel spindle.

(Figs. 27 and 37). A dentinal fiber is the cytoplasm of a pulp cell. Those cells of the pulp which lie next to the dentin have the somewhat surprising distinction of being cells of the dentin also. They are named *odontoblasts.* The nucleus of the odontoblast cell remains in the pulp surrounded by part of the cell's cytoplasm. The remainder of the cytoplasm of the odontoblast cell is stretched out like a long, thin tail and enters a dentinal tubule (Fig. 43). This cytoplasmic extension of the odontoblast is called a dentinal fiber (Tomes' fiber). Each dentinal fiber extends through the tubule to the dentinoenamel or dentinocemental junction. At their peripheral ends near the dentinoenamel and dentinocemental junctions the dentinal fibers are branched just as the dentinal tubules are branched (Fig. 37).

In some places in the crown of a tooth the peripheral ends of some dentinal fibers penetrate the dentinoenamel junction and protrude into the enamel. Here they appear as short, slightly thickened structures. These ends of dentinal fibers in the enamel are *enamel spindles* (Figs. 27, 28, 29 and 37).

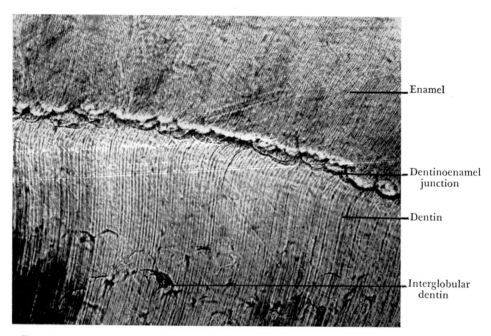

Enamel

Dentinoenamel junction

Dentin

Interglobular dentin

FIGURE 38.—Photomicrograph of part of a ground section of a tooth crown. The enamel is divided from the dentin by the scalloped dentinoenamel junction. Curvatures in the enamel rods are evident and in some areas cross-striations of the rods can be seen. In the dentin at the bottom of the picture are irregular areas (dark) of interglobular dentin. (Medium power magnification.)

In the crowns of some teeth the dentin has in it spots which are uncalcified or are hypocalcified (hypo = under, less than ordinary). These uncalcified spots, irregular in shape, usually occur in a layer a short distance inside the dentinoenamel junction (Figs. 16, 17, 18, 38 and 46). In this location such areas of uncalcified dentin are called *interglobular dentin*. The reason for the failure of proper calcification here is probably some metabolic disturbance which occurred at the time this part of the tooth was forming.

Root dentin invariably contains a band of minute uncalcified spots almost immediately beneath the cementum. This is called *Tomes' granular layer* (Fig. 16, 17, 18, 19, 39, 46 and 48). It was first described by the dental histologist Sir John Tomes (1815–1895) who thought that this region of the dentin had a granular appearance. Later it was found that this area is made up of very small uncalcified spots of dentin. Tomes' granular layer has considerable clinical importance which will be discussed later.

In the root dentin of some teeth a short distance beneath Tomes' granular layer there may be also a layer of interglobular dentin similar in size and configuration to the interglobular dentin found in the crown of the tooth (Fig. 39).

A modified type of dentin known as *secondary dentin* is usually found in older teeth along the pulpal wall of the dentin. Aside from the fact that in varying degrees it has fewer and less regular dentinal tubules than the first dentin produced, secondary dentin is similar to the earlier dentin. Secondary dentin may be formed throughout the life of the tooth as long

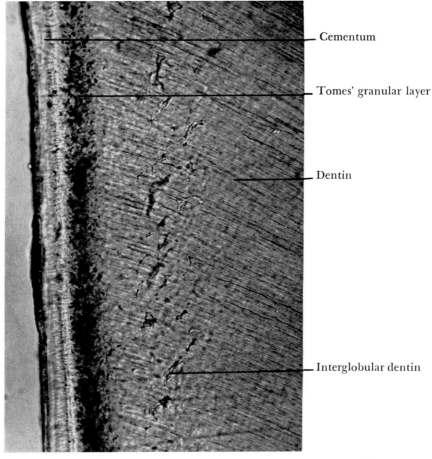

Cementum

Tomes' granular layer

Dentin

Interglobular dentin

FIGURE 39.—Photomicrograph of part of a ground section of tooth root. The cementum is the relatively narrow light band at the left of the picture; the dentin is the wide area at the right of the picture. In the dentin close to the cementum is the band of closely packed small areas of uncalcified dentin called Tomes' granular layer. Deeper in the dentin are larger, irregular areas of interglobular dentin (dark areas). Notice that the dentinal tubules are straight, and are not quite at right angles to the cementodentinal junction. In the cementum are small lines, perpendicular to the cementum surface, which are spaces once occupied by Sharpey's fibers (Chapter 6). (High power magnification.)

as the tooth pulp is intact. In posterior teeth it is formed most frequently in the pulp horns—that is, in the part of the pulp extending toward the cusp tips—and in the floor of the pulp chamber (Figs. 18, 23, and 44). In anterior teeth it is formed most frequently beneath the incisal edge when there has been considerable attrition (wearing off) (Fig. 40). Secondary dentin may occur also on the pulpal wall of dentin in areas where dental caries has started to penetrate the dentin at the dentinoenamel junction (Figs. 19 and 45). The formation of secondary dentin is often a result of the reaction of the tooth pulp to the irritation of attrition or of the caries process.

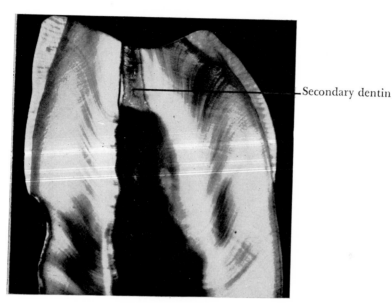

—Secondary dentin

FIGURE 40.—Photomicrograph of a ground section (cut faciolingually) of a canine tooth. Extensive attrition has resulted in the loss of the enamel and part of the dentin of the cusp. The formation of secondary dentin in the incisal part of the pulp cavity has protected the pulp from exposure. (Low power magnification.)

Sclerotic dentin is a modified dentin found in some areas of most old teeth and sometimes in young teeth. Dentin is said to be sclerotic when the dentinal fibers have degenerated and the dentinal tubules have become filled with calcium salts. Sclerotic dentin is often found beneath worn enamel such as occurs in the incisal area of anterior teeth, and beneath slowly progressing dental caries in locations where secondary dentin is being produced on the pulpal wall (Fig. 19). Sclerotic dentin is also found beneath Tomes' granular layer in the cervical area of older teeth where the cervical cementum has become exposed to the oral cavity as a result of recession of the gingiva. (Chapter 10).

In the mandibular incisor tooth shown in figure 41 the dentinal fibers have degenerated beneath the worn incisal edge, but the dentinal tubules have not become filled with calcium salts. Such an area has been referred to as a *dead tract*. The pulp beneath the dead tract in this tooth is protected by the presence of secondary dentin.

At the cervix on the facial side of this tooth there is a change in the dentin beneath the cervical abrasion. The white area, indicated by the pointer, is probably a dead tract. Outside of the dead tract, nearer the surface of the tooth, the dentin appears to be sclerotic—*i.e.*, the tubules are filled, or are becoming filled, with calcium salts.

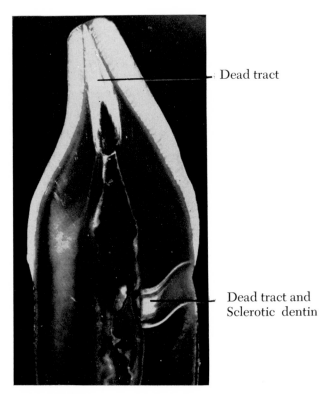

Dead tract

Dead tract and
Sclerotic dentin

FIGURE 41.—Photomicrograph of a ground section of a mandibular incisor tooth cut faciolingually. Beneath the worn incisal edge is a dead tract in the dentin. Deposition of secondary dentin beneath the dead tract has protected the pulp from damage. On the facial side of the tooth in the cervical area there is abrasion: the cementum is gone and some of the dentin has been worn away. (See Chapter 10, Figure 77.) Beneath this abraded surface there is an alteration in the dentin. Near the pulp is an area of dead tract, which appears white. Superficial (nearer the surface) to this dead tract the dentin seems to be sclerotic. On the pulp wall in this region secondary dentin has been produced; it protrudes into the pulp cavity inside the dead tract. Notice the curvature of the dentinal tubules in the cervical area. (Low power magnification.)

CLINICAL IMPORTANCE OF THE STRUCTURE OF DENTIN

From the point of view of the dental hygienist the structure of dentin is important because (1) it influences both the pattern of a carious lesion and the speed with which dental caries destroys a tooth; and (2) it accounts for the sensitivity frequently experienced by patients during the performance of an oral prophylaxis or during the eating of hot or cold foods.

In the preceding chapter it was explained that dental caries is a disease of the hard tissues of the tooth: acidogenic bacteria convert sugars into acids which dissolve the minerals out of the hard tooth tissues; and proteolytic (protein destroying) bacteria destroy the organic component of the hard tooth tissue in the same area.

When at any point the caries process has penetrated the enamel to the depth of the dentinoenamel junction, the caries-producing bacteria will also have reached this depth and will come in contact with the peripheral ends of the dentinal tubules. Since the bacteria are smaller than the diameter of the dentinal tubules they enter the tubules. The dentinal fibers which occupy the tubules are destroyed. The bacteria travel pulpward in the opened tubules and the dentin is slowly destroyed. Because the bacteria follow the course of the dentinal tubules, a carious lesion originating around a contact area or in the cervical area of a tooth extends in an apical direction as it approaches the pulp. Notice the direction of the dentinal tubules in Figures 19, 36, and 41).

The progress of dental caries through the dentin is often retarded, but not stopped, by defensive reactions that take place in the pulp. One such reaction is the production of *sclerotic dentin*. From the pulp tissue calcium salts are deposited in the dentinal tubules causing them to become filled with mineral substances, and so the progress of bacterial invasion is slowed down. Another defensive reaction against caries is the formation by the pulp of additional dentin, called *secondary dentin*, at the location where the bacteria-filled tubules reach the pulp. This increases the thickness of the dentin wall and helps to protect the tooth pulp, for a time at least, against the invasion of the disease. In a tooth from which the pulp has been removed these defensive reactions which are dependent upon the pulp cannot occur.

Another characteristic of dentin structure which is of particular interest to the dental hygienist is the location of Tomes' granular layer and its effect on the comfort of the patient. As we have seen, Tomes' granular layer consists of a narrow band of uncalcified areas in the root dentin immediately beneath the cementum. Now a natural aging process which occurs in nearly all mouths is the gradual recession of the gingiva and a resulting exposure of the cementum at the necks of the teeth. (This will be discussed in Chapter 10.) The dental hygienist in the performance of an oral prophylaxis finds it necessary to clean this exposed cervical cementum. This means that the hygienist is working very close to Tomes' granular layer which, being uncalcified and in close contact with the dentinal fibers, causes this area to be very sensitive. Therefore the patient may experience pain. The patient may also find this area of exposed cementum sensitive to hot or cold foods. A patient with exposed cervical cementum may believe that he has caries in this area because of the pain he experiences during eating or while brushing his teeth. These discomforts are more noticeable when the cervical cementum first becomes exposed. After the cervical cementum has been exposed to the oral environment for a few weeks or months the dentin beneath the exposed surface usually becomes sclerotic (Fig. 41) and the patient ceases to notice discomfort.

5

Tooth Pulp

The pulp of a tooth is located in the interior of the tooth. It occupies the pulp chamber in the crown and the root canal in the root of the tooth, and connects with the periodontal ligament at the apical foramen (Fig. 17).

COMPOSITION

Tooth pulp is the only noncalcified tissue of a tooth. It is a soft connective tissue, and like other connective tissues it is made up of *cells* and *intercellular substance* (Fig. 42). In young teeth the cells of the pulp tissue are more numerous than they are in older teeth and the intercellular substance is relatively smaller in amount.

While the *cells* of young pulp tissue are chiefly *fibroblasts*, specialized types of cells also are present: *histiocytes, undifferentiated mesenchymal cells, odontoblasts.*

The *intercellular substance* of the pulp consists of two kinds of material, the *amorphous substance* (= without form; structureless) and the *fibrous substance*. The amorphous substance is a jelly-like material in which are suspended all of the cellular and fibrous elements of the pulp tissue. The fibrous substance is a meshwork of minute fibrils. In the peripheral part of young pulp the fibrous substance is massed into little coiled, rope-like bundles called *Korff's fibers.*

Tooth pulp contains *blood vessels* and *nerves*. In many teeth there are also calcified structures called *denticles* (pulp stones) and *diffuse calcifications.*

STRUCTURES IN THE PULP

Fibroblast cells are more numerous than any other kind of cell in the pulp. Often they are described as star-shaped because of the irregular pointed outlines of their cytoplasm. Fibroblasts are responsible for the formation of the intercellular substance of pulp tissue.

Histiocytes and *undifferentiated mesenchymal cells* are located throughout the pulp near the capillaries. They are part of the pulp's defense mechanism and they respond to pulp injury by changing into defense cells of the sorts seen in any inflammatory reaction.

The *odontoblasts* are specialized fibroblasts which are located next to the dentin (Fig. 42). They are roughly cylindrical in shape, being somewhat longer than they are wide, and they contain an oval-shaped nucleus.

(68)

They are peculiar cells in that their cytoplasm does not remain entirely in the pulp. While part of the cytoplasm of the odontoblast remains surrounding the nucleus in the usual manner of cells, the remainder of it is stretched out in a long, thin tail which enters a dentinal tubule and extends in the tubule to the dentinoenamel or the dentinocemental junction (Figs. 37 and 43). This cytoplasmic tail of the odontoblast is called a *dentinal fiber*. When a dentinal fiber crosses the dentinoenamel junction into the enamel, the portion of it that is in the enamel is called an *enamel spindle* (Figs. 28, 29 and 37).

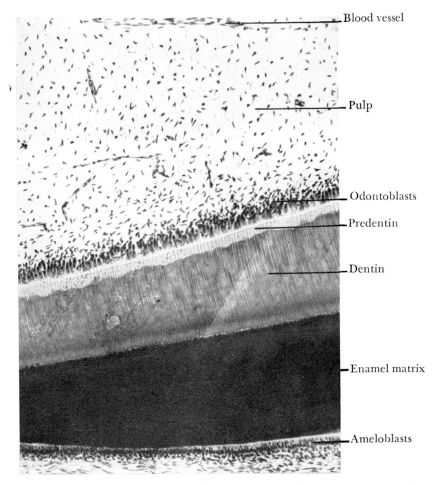

FIGURE 42. A section through a developing tooth of a pig. The tissues are very similar to those of a human tooth. The dark-stained, as yet uncalcified, enamel matrix is covered on its outer surface by the layer of ameloblasts which are beginning to lose their columnar shape. (See Chapter 11). The dentin contains dentinal tubules which extend from the dentinoenamel junction to the pulp. The layer of dentin next to the pulp is uncalcified, and is called pre-dentin, or dentinoid. In this section it is stained a lighter color than the earlier formed, calcified dentin. The pulp cells next to the predentin are the odontoblasts. Most of the other cells seen in the pulp are fibroblasts. Korff's fibers are not seen in this preparation. They require a special stain. Nerves are not seen in this preparation. Small blood vessels are scattered throughout the pulp tissue, and a larger blood vessel is seen at the top of the picture.

Korff's fibers are minute, rope-like, corkscrew-shaped structures which lie among the odontoblasts. They are produced by the merging of the fibrils of the fibrous intercellular substance of the pulp. Korff's fibers may be made visible for microscopic examination by special staining techniques applied to thin sections of young pulp tissue. They seem to have an important function in the formation of the dentin matrix. (See Chapter 11).

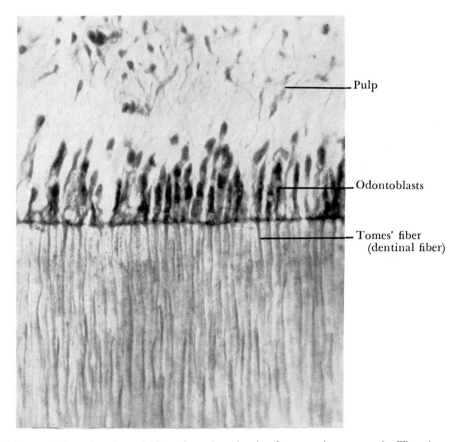

Figure 43. A section through the pulp and predentin of a young human tooth. The odontoblasts are dark-stained columnar cells. The nuclei and part of the cytoplasm of the odontoblasts are in the pulp. Long fibers of cytoplasm extend into the dentinal tubules. These are the *dentinal fibers*, or *Tomes' fibers*.

Blood vessels are plentiful in young pulp (Fig. 42). Small branches from the superior or the inferior alveolar artery enter the tooth through the apical foramen. They pass through the root canal to the pulp chamber and divide into capillaries. The circulating blood is collected into veins which pass out from the pulp through the apical foramen. *Lymphatic vessels* also have been demonstrated in the pulp.

Along with the blood vessels *nerves* enter the tooth pulp through the apical foramen giving it a rich nerve supply. These are branches of the second or third division of the fifth (trigeminal) cranial nerve. Just beneath the layer of odontoblast cells around the edge of the pulp the nerves in the pulp form a network with some nerve fibers having endings on the odontoblasts. This arrangement helps to account for the sensitivity of the dentin, since the odontoblasts have part of their cytoplasm in the dentinal tubules. Whether or not nerves extend into the dentinal tubules is a subject of controversy.

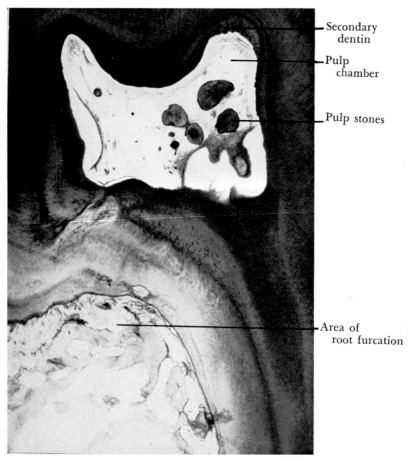

FIGURE 44.—A longitudinal section of a human molar tooth. This was an old tooth. The soft pulp tissue has been shrunken and damaged in the preparation of the tissue, but the denticles (pulp stones) are clearly seen. Secondary dentin is seen in the pulp horns. This section was cut at such an angle that it does not pass through the narrow root canal, but of course a root canal was present. The lower left corner of the picture is the area of the root furcation.

Denticles are calcified structures of an irregularly rounded shape commonly found in tooth pulp (Figs. 19 and 44). They may lie free in the soft tissue or they may be attached to the dentin wall. They vary in shape and size, the size increasing with the age of the tooth. Generally they are regarded as of little clinical importance excepting as they may interfere with endodontic treatment. They are never a source of infection.

Diffuse calcifications are small, thin scatterings of calcified material frequently found in the pulps of older teeth, usually in the root canals (Figs. 19 and 45). Clinically they are usually unimportant.

FUNCTIONS OF THE PULP

Tooth pulp has several functions. For purposes of description these functions may be listed as follows: (1) formative, (2) sensory, (3) nutritive, (4) defensive.

The *formative function*. Tooth pulp forms the dentin of the tooth, as will be explained in the discussion of tooth development to be found in Chapter 11. We will see that Korff's fibers, which are composed of the fibrillar material of the intercellular substance, give rise to the fibrils of the dentin matrix. The pulp also produces the amorphous cementing substance of the dentin matrix. And the odontoblast cells of the pulp have their cytoplasm stretched out into thin, thread-like extensions which are the dentinal fibers that occupy the dentinal tubules.

The *sensory function*. Tooth pulp is very sensitive to external stimuli. The nerves in the pulp are responsible for the sensation experienced by an individual when a stimulus is applied to the tooth. It is an interesting fact that the sensation educed by stimuli received by a tooth pulp is a sensation of pain. A person cannot differentiate between extremes of heat (hot coffee) and of cold (ice cream) applied to the tooth. If sensation is experienced it is merely pain in both cases. Slight pressures on a tooth will produce a sensation of pressure or touch. Most of this sensation is due to pressure on the periodontal ligament.

The *nutritive function*. Since tooth pulp is a living tissue with a blood supply, it receives nutrients from the blood stream. It may be supposed that nutrients enter the dentinal tubules either by way of the cytoplasmic dentinal fibers or around the outside of the dentinal fibers. Such nutrients may be carried in this way as far as the dentinoenamel and dentino-cemental junctions. There is a good deal yet to be learned about this subject.

Since unwarranted deductions are sometimes made from a set of briefly presented facts such as those given above, it should be made clear that whatever the manner of nutrition of the dentin this is a matter entirely apart from the question of dental caries. We cannot associate the nutritive function of the pulp and the general nutrition of the individual with the presence or absence of dental caries activity. Such association should not be attempted from the above discussion. Dental caries is a disease which starts on the outside surface of the tooth and is a process of an entirely different nature.

The *defensive function*. Defense reactions of the pulp are expressed in several ways: pulp may show an inflammatory reaction; pulp may change the character of existing dentin; pulp may produce additional dentin (secondary dentin).

In case of pulp damage the pulp shows an inflammatory reaction. Cells appear which are commonly found at any site of inflammation. Some of these defense cells are derived from histiocytes and undifferentiated mesenchymal cells of the pulp; some are carried into the pulp by the blood stream from their points of origin in the bone marrow and lymph nodes. As the defense cells become effective in controlling the damaging process, the pulp may produce sclerosis of the existing dentin and may also lay down secondary dentin along the pulpal wall.

Sclerosis (sclero = hard) of the dentin involves the filling in of the dentinal tubules, usually in a restricted area, with calcium salts so that the dentin in this area is a solid calcified tissue instead of a tissue perforated with tubules which contain dentinal fibers (Fig. 19). Sclerotic dentin usually occurs beneath a carious lesion and its presence tends to retard the progress of the destruction of the tooth tissue. The stimulus to the pulp which causes the production of sclerosis is received through the dentinal tubules.

Pulpal to the sclerotic dentin the pulp may produce, as a defensive re-action, varying amounts of secondary dentin which gives the pulp addi-tional protection against external irritation. The formation of secondary dentin and sclerotic dentin occur in aging teeth, where infection is not a factor, as a result of the stimulation produced by attrition (Fig. 41).

AGE CHANGES IN THE PULP

Just as age brings about changes in other parts of the body, it brings about changes in the pulps of teeth. These changes are universal and normal and are not to be regarded as pathologic. The continued formation of secondary dentin with increasing age causes the pulp chamber to become smaller and the root canals to become narrower. In some old teeth which show heavy attrition or dental caries of long standing, the pulp chamber may be entirely filled by the deposition of secondary dentin. The cells of the pulp, very numerous in young teeth, decrease in number with age, and the fibrous intercellular substance is relatively increased. Old tooth pulps are composed mostly of fibrous intercellular substance. The blood supply of the pulp decreases with age. Denticles are larger and more numerous in old teeth and diffuse calcifications are increased. These changes of the pulp do not alter the function of the tooth.

CLINICAL IMPORTANCE OF THE PULP

A fully developed tooth may function for many years after its pulp has been removed and the pulp canal filled. Although the enamel of the tooth becomes more brittle, its function is not affected by the loss of the pulp. The cementum is not affected, nor is the process of continued cementum formation. A tooth without a pulp cannot, however, produce secondary dentin or sclerotic dentin. Loss of a tooth pulp usually comes about as a result of caries or of tooth fracture, with accompanying pulp infection. Careful treatment by the dentist is essential in either case to prevent the infection from travelling through the root canal and apical foramen into the tissues surrounding the tooth, with a consequent loss of the tooth.

6

Cementum

LOCATION

Cementum is the thin layer of calcified tissue, often about as thick as a coat of paint, which makes up the surface of the root of a tooth (Fig. 16, 39 and 46). It overlies and is attached to the root dentin. In the area of the cementoenamel junction the cementum may have any one of three relationships with the enamel of the tooth crown: it may exactly meet the enamel; it may not quite meet the enamel, leaving a little dentin exposed; or it may slightly overlap the enamel (Figs. 16, 18, 45, 46, 47 and 47A). This last arrangement is the most common.

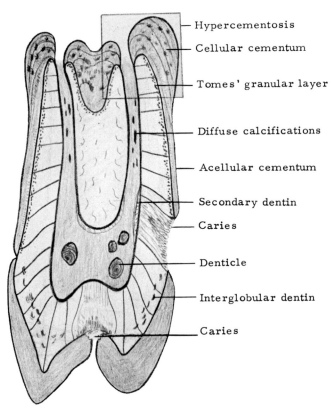

— Hypercementosis

— Cellular cementum

— Tomes' granular layer

— Diffuse calcifications

— Acellular cementum

— Secondary dentin

— Caries

— Denticle

— Interglobular dentin

— Caries

FIGURE 45.—Diagrammatic drawing of a longitudinal faciolingual section of a maxillary first premolar tooth. The tip of the lingual root shows a very large amount of cementum, which is sometimes referred to as hypercementosis. For a photomicrograph of such thick cementum see Figures 48 and 50.

COMPOSITION

Like enamel, dentin, and bone, cementum is made up of *organic matrix* which contains crystallized mineral substances. Cementum may have cells, called *cementocytes*, irregularly scattered through it. It does not contain blood vessels or nerves. Cementum is not quite so hard as dentin, being about 50 per cent inorganic (mineral) material and about 50 per cent organic substance and water. This is about the same hardness as bone.

STRUCTURE OF CEMENTUM

Compared to the structure of dentin the structure of cementum has some similarities and some differences. Like dentin, the organic matrix of

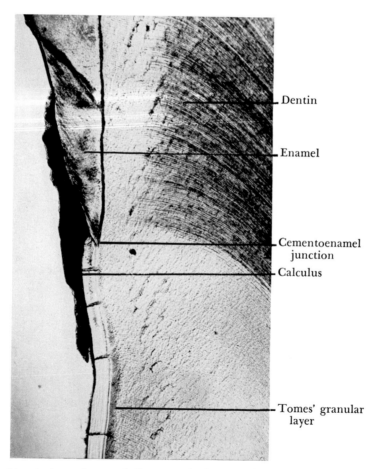

FIGURE 46.—A photomicrograph (low power) of a ground section of a tooth in the area of the cementoenamel junction. The cementum overlaps the enamel slightly. Calculus adheres to both the enamel and the cementum. The four conspicuous lines in the cementum are cracks produced by the grinding of the section. Tomes' granular layer lies beneath the cementum in the dentin. Deeper in the dentin in both the root and the crown are irregular dark areas of interglobular dentin. The dentinal tubules are distinct. The darkness of the tubules in the upper right is a result of air in the tubules due to the preparation of the section; it is not due to any structural change.

cementum is composed of a framework of fine fibrils held together by
an amorphous cementing substance which becomes calcified. Unlike
dentin, cementum may contain whole cells. You will recall that dentin
contains processes of pulp cells but it does not contain entire cells.

Cementum is a product of the periodontal ligament, which is the layer
of connective tissue that lies between the tooth root and the bony socket

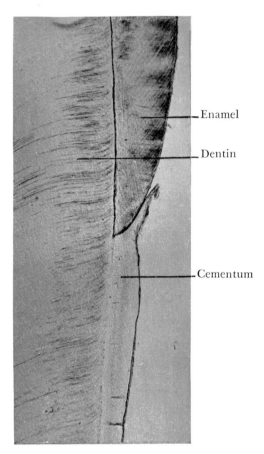

Enamel

Dentin

Cementum

FIGURE 47.—A photomicrograph of a ground section of a tooth in the area of the cementoenamel junction. The cementum overlaps the enamel considerably. The separation of the
cementum from the enamel at the border of the cementum is an artifact probably caused by
the drying of the specimen during preparation of the section; in life the cementum was no
doubt fixed firmly against the enamel surface.

in which the root is set. Certain cells of the periodontal ligament (*cementoblasts*) which lie close to the tooth root become converted into cells of the
cementum (*cementocytes*) as the cementum is being formed.

Cementocytes are connected with one another by numerous thread-like
projections of their cytoplasm. The space in the cementum which is
occupied by the body of the cementocyte is called a *lacuna* (little space);
and the spaces occupied by the cytoplasmic projections of the cementocyte
are called *canaliculi* (little canals). Canaliculi of adjacent lacunæ may

join and thus connect neighboring lacunæ. In cementum most of the canaliculi are directed toward the periodontal ligament (Figs. 16, 17, 48 and 49).

Ordinarily cementocytes are not found throughout the entire cementum on the tooth root. Usually the thin cementum on the cervical portion

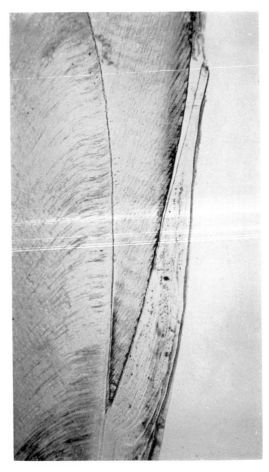

FIGURE 47*A*.—A photomicrograph of a ground section of a tooth in the area of the cementoenamel junction. The cementum on this tooth overlaps the enamel to an unusual extent. Not many teeth show this amount of overlapping. The separation of the cementum from the enamel is probably due to the drying of the specimen during preparation. In life the cementum undoubtedly was firm against the enamel. This is the mesial surface of a mandibular molar tooth.

of the root has no cementocytes, or only a few. In the apical portion of the root the cementum is usually relatively thick, and while in this region the cementum close to the dentin may have few cementocytes, the outer layers often contain many irregularly distributed cementocytes. Cementum which contains cementocytes is called *cellular cementum*, and cementum which has no cementocytes is called *acellular cementum* (Figs. 16, 17, 18, 45, 48, and 49).

The outer surface of cementum, next to the periodontal ligament, remains less calcified than the rest of the cementum and is called *cementoid*.

Visible in the cementum by microscopic examination are structures
called *Sharpey's fibers* (Fig. 39). These are the ends of bundles of fibers of
the periodontal ligament which have become embedded in the cementum
during its formation. They attach the periodontal ligament firmly to the
tooth.

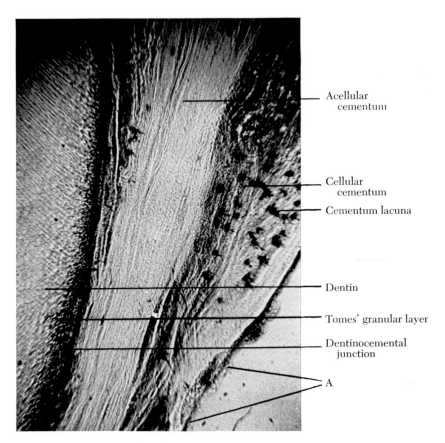

Acellular
cementum

Cellular
cementum

Cementum lacuna

Dentin

Tomes' granular layer

Dentinocemental
junction

A

FIGURE 48.—A photomicrograph of an area of thick cementum on a tooth root. Taken
from an area similar to that shown at the tip of the lingual root of the tooth in Figure 45.
A indicates the surface of the tooth root to which the periodontal ligament was attached.

CLINICAL IMPORTANCE OF CEMENTUM

The cementum is part of the mechanism by which a tooth is attached
in the tooth socket. Just as the periodontal ligament is attached to the
tooth by Sharpey's fibers embedded in the cementum, it is similarly attached to the tooth socket by Sharpey's fibers embedded in the bone (Figs.
52 and 53). The result of this double attachment is that the tooth is
literally suspended in its socket (Chapter 7).

Cementum probably continues to be intermittently produced by the periodontal ligament throughout the life of the tooth. Additions of cementum at the root apex cause a slow occlusal movement of the tooth that partially compensates for the loss of crown length which results from attrition during years of use.

Cementum also repairs damage to the tooth root: it may replace lost areas of tooth root which have been resorbed following injury. While

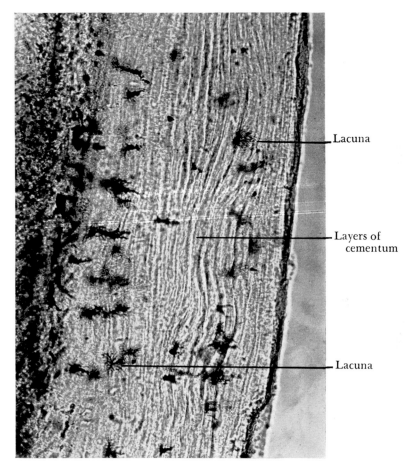

FIGURE 49.—A photomicrograph of an area of cementum seen with a higher power objective than the one used for Figure 48. Notice the canaliculi leading from the lacunæ; and notice that they often are directed chiefly toward the outside surface of the root (to the right). The layer upon layer formation of cementum is clear.

normal vertical pressures or light lateral pressures do not result in damage to the tooth root, a severe lateral pressure on a tooth may result not only in resorption of the bone of the tooth socket, but also in a localized resorption of the tooth root. Underlying dentin, as well as cementum, may be resorbed in some cases. When the cause of the resorption is removed, if the damage has not been too extensive, new cementum may be laid down over the damaged area, replacing both the lost cementum and the lost dentin.

The presence of cementoid on the outer surface of the root is an important factor in the clinical success of orthodontic treatment. Cementoid, because it is only slightly calcified, undergoes resorption less readily than bone. When the orthodontist establishes continued light lateral pressure on a tooth by the use of orthodontic appliances, the pressure is transmitted to the periodontal ligament and to the bone of the tooth socket, and the bone, not the tooth root, is resorbed. On the opposite side of the tooth

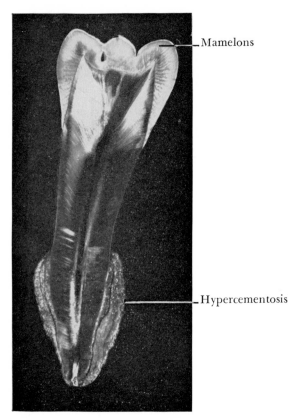

FIGURE 50.—A photomicrograph (low power) of a ground section of a mandibular incisor tooth cut mesiodistally. Before this tooth was cut the apical half of the root looked like a round ball on the end of the tooth. This is hypercementosis. Notice, also, the conspicuous mamelons, and the pit between the left and center mamelon.

socket, where the periodontal ligament is under tension (pull) due to this lateral movement, addition of bone takes place, and there is thereby an actual change in the location of the tooth socket and in the position of the tooth (Chapter 8). The difference between the pressure used by the orthodontist and the pressure which causes damage to the tooth root lies chiefly in the difference in the severity of the pressure.

Cementum is sometimes formed in excessive amounts. Excessive cementum is variously called *hypercementosis*, *excementosis*, or *cementum hyperplasia*. It may occur on all or on only a few of the teeth in any mouth; and it may occur over the entire tooth root or only in localized areas (Fig.

45). The cause of excessive cementum formation is not fully known. A large amount of cementum sometimes is useful in that it may furnish additional attachment for periodontal ligament fibers. Again, it may be a handicap. If it occurs as a spicule protruding from the side of the root and interlocking in a resorbed area of the lamina dura (the bone of the tooth socket), or if it occurs as excessive cementum at the root apex producing a ball-shaped root end (Fig. 50), it may create a problem in extraction if for any reason the tooth must be removed.

Cementicles are small bodies of cementum which are sometimes found in the periodontal ligament. They are usually regarded as of no clinical importance.

7

Periodontal Ligament

(Periodontal Membrane)

LOCATION

The periodontal ligament (peri = around; odontos = tooth) is a layer of connective tissue about $\frac{1}{100}$ inch in width which surrounds the root of a tooth, occupying the space between the tooth root and the bone of the tooth socket (Figs. 51, 55, 65). The periodontal ligament is also called *periodontal membrane*.

STRUCTURE OF THE PERIODONTAL LIGAMENT

The periodontal ligament is made up of cells and of amorphous and fibrous intercellular substance. The most outstanding constituent is the fibrous intercellular substance which makes up the *fibers* of the periodontal ligament. Among these fibers are located *fibroblast cells*, *blood vessels*, *lymph vessels*, *nerves*, and in some areas small groups or strings of *epithelial cells*, and sometimes *cementicles*. In addition to these structures there are often specialized cells, which function in the formation of cementum (cementoblasts) and of bone (osteoblasts); and sometimes there are specialized cells associated with the resorption of cementum (cementoclasts) and of bone (osteoclasts).

In width the periodontal ligament has been found to range from 0.12 to 0.33 mm. The width varies on different teeth and in different areas around the same tooth. Decreased function of the tooth seems to be accompanied by decreased width of the periodontal ligament.

Bundles of periodontal ligament fibers are attached at one side of the periodontal ligament to the cementum covering the tooth root; and with the exception of certain fibers around the cervix of the tooth they are attached at the other side of the periodontal ligament to the bone of the tooth socket (Fig. 51). This attachment takes place when the cementum and the bone are forming: ends of bundles of the periodontal ligament fibers become entrapped in the forming hard tissue. This attachment serves to hold the tooth firmly in the jaw. These attached heavy fiber bundles of the periodontal ligament are referred to collectively as *Sharpey's fibers* (Figs. 52, 53).

While large bundles of fibers are attached to both cementum and bone, it does not thereby follow that each fiber of each bundle extends uninterrupted from cementum to bone. As a matter of fact, the individual fibers extend from the cementum or from the bone toward the center of the periodontal ligament where probably their ends are interwoven with

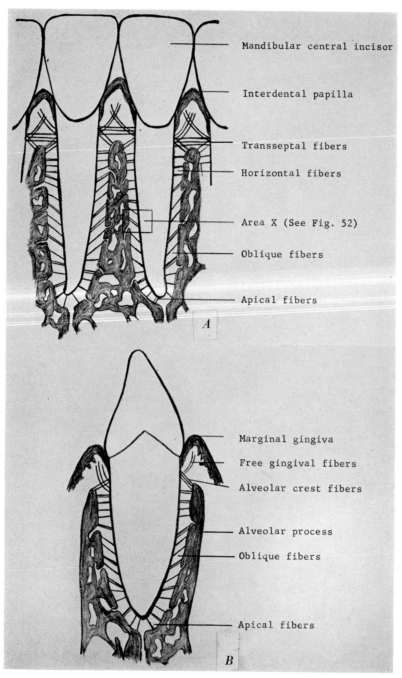

Mandibular central incisor

Interdental papilla

Transseptal fibers

Horizontal fibers

Area X (See Fig. 52)

Oblique fibers

Apical fibers

A

Marginal gingiva

Free gingival fibers

Alveolar crest fibers

Alveolar process

Oblique fibers

Apical fibers

B

FIGURE 51.—A diagrammatic illustration of the arrangement of the periodontal ligament fibers around the tooth roots of the mandibular incisors. The width of the periodontal ligament is exaggerated in order to show the direction of the fibers. *A*. A facial view. *B*. Proximal view. Area X in Figure *A* is shown in detail in Figure 52. (Adapted from Noyes, Schour, Noyes.)

ends of fibers from the opposite direction.   This area of interwoven fibers
is called the *intermediate plexus*.   The fact that the bundles are spliced
in the center of the periodontal ligment enables a readjustment of these
fibers as a tooth moves occlusally in eruption.

Around a nonfunctioning tooth (one which is not in occlusion with the
teeth in the opposing arch) the periodontal ligament fibers are relaxed and

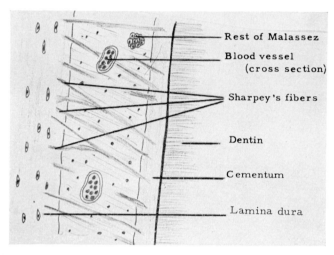

FIGURE 52.—Diagrammatic drawing of a small area of periodontal ligament showing Sharpey's
fibers. Enlargement of area X in Figure 51*A*.

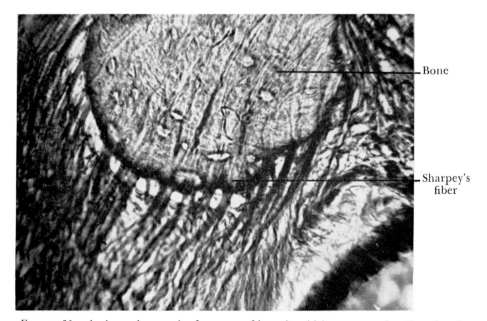

FIGURE 53.—A photomicrograph of an area of bone in which numerous bundles of periodontal ligament fibers are embedded. The embedded ends of these fiber bundles are known
as *Sharpey's fibers*. As seen here the strength of this attachment is impressive. (High power
magnification.)

wavy, with no definite orientation (Fig. 61); but around a tooth which is in heavy function the larger bundles are stretched straight and have a characteristic orientation on different areas of the tooth root. These large, well-oriented bundles of fibers are referred to as the *principal fibers of the periodontal ligament.*

Principal Fibers of the Periodontal Ligament

The principal fibers of the periodontal ligament around a heavily functioning tooth have such a clear and consistant arrangement that they have been described as being composed of six groups of fibers, each group being named according to its location and orientation: (1) the *free gingival fibers*, (2) the *transseptal fibers*, (3) the *alveolar crest fibers*, (4) the *horizontal fibers*, (5) the *oblique fibers*, and (6) the *apical fibers*. Study the position of these groups of fibers in Figures 51A and B as you read their description in the text.

1. *Free gingival fibers* are located around the cervical part of the root. Bundles of these fibers are embedded at one end in the cementum. The fibers extend from the cementum out into the gingiva which surrounds the neck of the tooth. In the gingiva the heavy bundles of fibers separate into individual fibers and intermingle with the connective tissue fibers of the gingiva. Examine Figures 51A and 73 for the location and arrangement of the free gingival fibers. Notice that a pressure applied on the incisal (or occlusal) part of the tooth would cause the free gingival fibers to be stretched taunt with the result that this group of fibers would function to hold the gingiva firmly to the tooth surface.

2. *Transseptal fibers* are located just apical to the gingival fiber group and are on the mesial and distal sides of the tooth only. Bundles of these fibers are embedded at one end in the cementum of one tooth and at the other end in the cementum of the adjacent tooth. With the exception of the maxillary and mandibular central incisors, where the mesial sides of the right and left centrals are connected by these fibers, the transseptal fibers extend from the cementum on the mesial side of one tooth to the cementum on the distal side of the adjacent tooth. Notice in Figure 51A how they cross over the top of the bone between the teeth. These fibers help to maintain the teeth in their proper relationship to one another.

3. *Alveolar crest fibers* are located at the level of the alveolar crest (the margin of the bone which surrounds the tooth root). These fiber bundles are embedded on one side of the periodontal ligament in the cementum of the tooth root and on the other side of the periodontal ligament in the alveolar crest. They are of course found all around the tooth. Examine Figures 51A and B and notice how the arrangement of this group of fibers helps to resist horizontal movements of the tooth.

4. *Horizontal fibers* are located apical to the alveolar crest fibers. They are embedded in the cementum of the tooth root and in the bone of the tooth socket. They lie in a horizontal position relative to the jaw bone. They are of course all around the tooth root. Examine the arrangement of these fibers in Figure 51A and you will see how they function to resist horizontal pressures applied to the tooth crown.

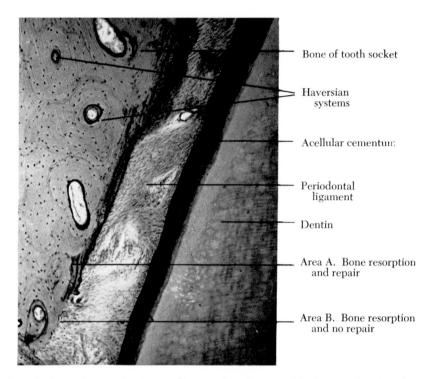

Bone of tooth socket

Haversian
systems

Acellular cementum

Periodontal
ligament

Dentin

Area A. Bone resorption
and repair

Area B. Bone resorption
and no repair

FIGURE 54.—A photomicrograph of a small area of tooth root with the associated periodontal ligament and lamina dura. The direction of the periodontal ligament fibers tells us
that the crown of the tooth was at the bottom of the pictured area. Notice the resorption
of the bone of the alveolar crest at *area B*. At *area A* there has been bone resorption as far
as the end of the pointer line; and then there was bone apposition (addition) on the surface
of the resorbed area (repair).

5. *Oblique fibers* are located immediately apical to the horizontal group
of fibers. They are attached to the cementum and to the bone of the tooth
socket and they run in an oblique, or diagonal, direction. Look at the
orientation of these fibers in Figures 51*A* and *B*: the end attached to the
bone is always more toward the tooth crown than is the end attached to
the cementum. Imagine a pressure applied vertically to the incisal (or
occlusal) surface of the tooth. Such a pressure would stretch the oblique
fibers taunt and the tooth would be literally suspended in its socket
(Fig. 54). The result of such vertical pressure is a pull on, rather than a
pressure on, both the cementum of the tooth root and the bone of the
alveolus (tooth socket). This pull (tension) is fortunate, because continued pressure on bone ordinarily results in bone resorption. This group
of strong oblique fiber bundles prevents the apex of the root from being
jammed against the bottom of the socket.

At the transition between the oblique fibers and the radiating apical
fibers there is a small region in which the fibers again extend in a horizontal
plane. Although these fibers are usually not named in the arbitrary
classification which has been given to the periodontal ligament fibers,

they function with the previously described horizontal fibers in stabilizing the tooth.

6. *Apical fibers* radiate around the apex of the tooth. At approximately right angles to their attachment in the cementum they extend to their attachment in the bone at the base of the alveolus. As you can see by examining Figures 51*A* and *B* these apical fibers resist any force tending to lift the tooth from the socket, and function with the fibers of other groups to stabilize the tooth against forces tending to produce a tilting movement.

Scattered among the principal fibers of the periodontal ligament are other smaller fibers which have no distinct orientation.

STRUCTURES IN THE PERIODONTAL LIGAMENT

Blood vessels of the periodontal ligament are branches of the superior or the inferior alveolar artery and vein. They enter the periodontal ligament at various locations: (1) at the fundus (bottom) of the alveolus, along with vessels which supply the tooth pulp; (2) through openings in the bone of the sides of the alveolus, coming from the bone marrow spaces; and (3) from the deeper branches of gingival blood vessels which pass over the alveolar crest.

Lymphatic vessels follow the path of the blood vessels.

Nerves of the periodontal ligament generally follow the blood vessels. They are sensory nerves from the second or third division of the fifth (trigeminal) cranial nerve. They provide a sense of touch—that is, they enable an individual to be aware of a touch or a tap given to the tooth.

Rests of Malessez are small groups of epithelial cells which are seen in microscopic examination of the periodontal ligament (Figs. 52, 74 and 76). They are sometimes called *epithelial rests*. At times such epithelial cells are seen microscopically as strings of cells rather than as round groups of cells in the periodontal ligament, in which case they are referred to as remains of *Hertwig's epithelial root sheath* (Fig. 74*B*). Whatever name is applied to these epithelial cells found in the periodontal ligament, they have come to be recognized as cells derived from the enamel organ which produced the tooth enamel at the time the tooth was forming (Chapter 11). Their presence may be important pathologically in the formation of certain tumors and cyst linings.

Cementicles are minute calcified bodies sometimes seen in microscopic examination of the periodontal ligament of older individuals. Cementicles may be attached to the cementum, or they may be entirely separate from the tooth root. Their size varies but their shape is ordinarily spherical. Usually they are not considered to be of clinical importance.

Osteoblasts (osteo = bone; blast = germ) are specialized connective tissue cells which are found at the surface of bone in locations where bone formation is occurring. They may be seen in the periodontal ligament at the surface of the bone of the tooth socket in locations where bone is being laid down. *Osteoclasts* (clast = break) are specialized connective tissue cells which border bone which is being resorbed. They may occur in the periodontal ligament next to the bone of the tooth socket in locations where bone resorption is taking place. Similarly, *cementoblasts* are specialized connective tissue cells which accompany cementum formation, and *cementoclasts* are specialized connective tissue cells which accompany cementum resorption. These cells occur in the periodontal ligament at the surface of the cementum where cementum formation or cementum resorption is taking place.

FUNCTIONS AND CLINICAL IMPORTANCE OF THE PERIODONTAL LIGAMENT

The functions of the periodontal ligament may be described under five headings: (1) supportive, (2) formative, (3) resorptive, (4) sensory, and (5) nutritive.

The *supportive function* of the periodontal ligament results from the ingenious arrangement of its principal fibers. As you have seen, the fibers are so arranged that functional pressure on the tooth crown from any direction produces a tension (pulling) of certain fiber groups. Consequently, pressure on the tooth crown is transmitted to the bone of the tooth socket and to the cementum as a pull. Due to this fiber arrangement which suspends the tooth in its socket the tooth is not pressed against the bone of the socket wall during the process of biting and chewing. These sturdy principal fibers of the periodontal ligament which separate the cementum of the tooth root from the wall of the socket by about 1/100 inch are able to withstand the tremendous force produced by the powerful jaw muscles in closing the jaws. It has been determined that the maximum biting force between the molar teeth in a group of 100 adult American men varied around 150 pounds. In a group of Eskimos on their original native diet the force was much greater.

A sudden excessive pressure applied to a tooth crown, such as in case of an accidental blow, may damage the periodontal ligament sufficiently to loosen the tooth.

The *formative function* of the periodontal ligament is seen in both the developing tooth and in the adult functioning tooth. During tooth development the periodontal ligament produces both the cementum of the tooth root and the bone of the tooth socket. In the functioning tooth the periodontal ligament is able to produce cementum at any time during the life of the tooth; and it maintains the bone of the tooth socket by producing new bone following bone resorption (Fig. 54).

The *resorptive function* of the periodontal ligament accompanies the formative function. Whereas tension (pull) on the periodontal ligament fibers tends to stimulate cementum and bone formation, pressure stimulates bone resorption. Severe pressure produces rapid bone resorption, and sometimes may cause resorption of the more resistant cementum. If sufficiently severe, pressure may destroy areas of the periodontal ligament. More will be learned about the processes of bone formation and bone resorption in the discussion of bone and the alveolar process (Chapter 8).

The *sensory function* of the periodontal ligament is seen in the ability of an individual to estimate the amount of pressure in mastication and to identify which of several teeth receives a slight tap with an instrument.

The *nutritive function* is served by the presence of blood vessels in the periodontal ligament.

It is evident that without the periodontal ligament a tooth cannot be retained in its socket. Localized destruction of the periodontal ligament may be repaired by the formation of new tissue when the cause of the destruction is removed. Localized detachment from the cementum of the principal fibers of the periodontal ligament may be followed by fiber reattachment if removal of irritating factors permits the formation of new cementum. Extensive destruction of the periodontal ligament may result in the necessity for the removal of the tooth.

8

Bone and the Alveolar Process

BONE

The word *bone* is used to designate both a tissue and an organ. *Bone,* a tissue, is one of the connective tissues. It is made up of (1) an organic matrix which calcifies and (2) osteocytes (bone cells). *A bone,* an organ, such as the mandible, for example, is composed of bone tissue; it contains in its center bone marrow, and it has closely associated with it blood vessels and nerves.

GROSS STRUCTURE OF A BONE (an organ)

Bones are solid-looking organs, but they are not solid structures throughout. The bone tissue of which bones are composed may be described in two classes: (1) *compact bone* and (2) *trabecular bone* (or *cancellous bone*). The outside wall of a bone, the mandible, for example, is compact bone; but the mandible has a hollow center, the *bone marrow cavity*, into which *trabeculæ* (spicules) of bone protrude. These trabeculæ make up trabecular bone. In the spaces around the trabeculæ in the bone marrow cavity is the *bone marrow.*

Examine Figure 55 which is a drawing of a cross section of a human mandible, and Figure 65 which is a drawing of a longitudinal section of a human mandible. Notice the compact character of the bone which comprises the outer wall of the mandible. The number and size of the trabeculæ in the marrow cavity of a bone are determined to a large degree by the functional activity of the organ: the greater the functional activity the greater the number of trabeculæ.

Certain advantages result from this arrangement of bone tissue into compact and trabecular bone. For one thing, a large bone with trabeculæ and bone marrow in its center is much lighter in weight than would be the same organ composed of solid bone tissue throughout. Also, the presence of the bone marrow makes available to the bone tissue nutrition from blood vessels which are located inside the organ as well as from blood vessels which lie on the outside surface.

The outside surface of all bones is covered by a thin connective tissue membrane called the *periosteum* (peri = around; osteum = bone). The inside surfaces of bones are covered with a much more delicate connective tissue membrane called the *endosteum* (endo = within) (Fig. 55).

MICROSCOPIC STRUCTURE OF BONE (a tissue)

Bone tissue consists of bone cells and a bone matrix which is made up of two kinds of intercellular substance, fibrous and amorphous. The intercellular substance becomes calcified, which makes bone a hard tissue. Bone is about 50 per cent mineral substance and about 50 per cent organic substance. It has about the same hardness as cementum.

The cells of bone tissue, *osteocytes* (osteo = bone; cyte = cell), are distributed throughout the calcified intercellular substance. The space in

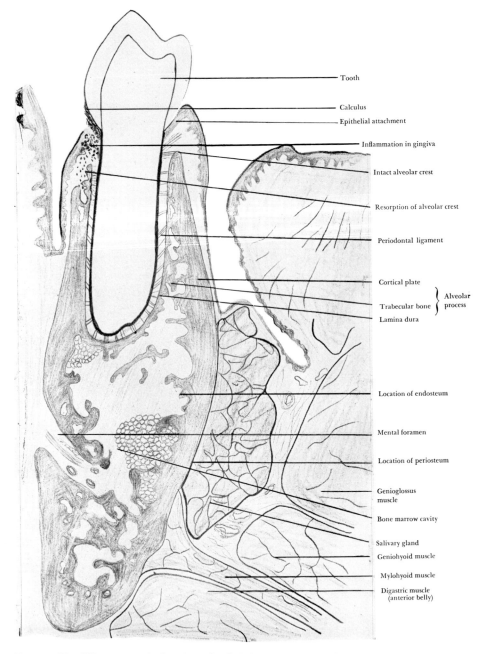

Tooth

Calculus

Epithelial attachment

Inflammation in gingiva

Intact alveolar crest

Resorption of alveolar crest

Periodontal ligament

Cortical plate

Trabecular bone } Alveolar process

Lamina dura

Location of endosteum

Mental foramen

Location of periosteum

Genioglossus muscle

Bone marrow cavity

Salivary gland

Geniohyoid muscle

Mylohyoid muscle

Digastric muscle (anterior belly)

FIGURE 55.—Diagrammatic drawing of a faciolingual section of a human mandible in the region of the first premolar tooth (much enlarged). This section is not cut through the pulp cavity of the tooth.

the bone matrix which is occupied by an osteocyte is called a *lacuna* (little space) (Figs. 57 and 58). Lacunæ are connected with one another by a system of *canaliculi* (little canals). These canaliculi extend not only from one lacuna to another, but some of them open into the various canals of bone where capillaries are located. Tissue fluids pass from the capillaries to the canaliculi and from one lacuna to another throughout the bone tissue.

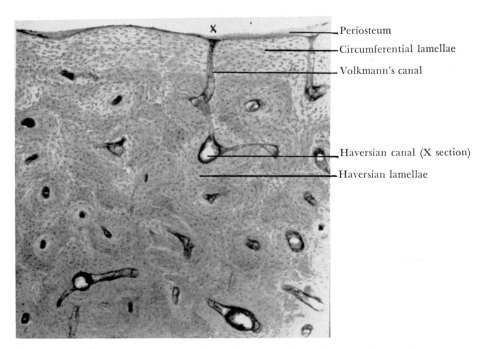

Periosteum

Circumferential lamellae

Volkmann's canal

Haversian canal (X section)

Haversian lamellae

FIGURE 56.—Photomicrograph of a ground cross section of human femur. (Low power magnification.) At the top of the picture is the bone surface with a portion of the periosteum still adhering to it in some places. The bone lamellæ at the surface have a circumferential arrangement. Beneath the circumferential lamellæ are Haversian systems where the lamellæ are in concentric layers. In the center of each Haversian system is the Haversian canal. In several places a Volkmann's canal enters an Haversian canal. Near the bottom of the picture Volkmann's canals are entering an Haversian canal from two directions. In the upper right two Volkmann's canals enter from the outside of the organ.. The one marked *x* is seen in higher magnification in figure 57.

Mature bone tissue is made up of thin layers, called *lamellæ*. These lamellæ have two different patterns of arrangement, and according to their pattern bone tissue is called either *Haversian system bone* or *lamellar bone*.

In *Haversian system bone* the lamellæ are arranged in concentric circles around a very small central canal which is called an *Haversian canal*. A series of concentric lamellæ with the included Haversian canal is called an *Haversian system* (Figs. 56, 57 and 58). An Haversian system may have from 4 to 20 concentric lamellæ and may measure somewhat more or less than 0.1 mm. in diameter.

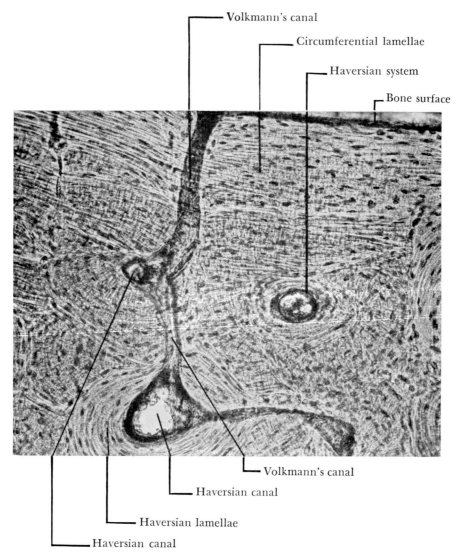

Volkmann's canal

Circumferential lamellae

Haversian system

Bone surface

Volkmann's canal

Haversian canal

Haversian lamellae

Haversian canal

FIGURE 57.—This photomicrograph of a ground section of bone is a higher magnification of the area marked x in figure 56. The surface of the bone is seen in the upper right. A Volkmann's canal cuts through the surface circumferential lamellæ and enters an Haversian canal slightly at left of center. The Volkmann's canal continues (toward bottom of picture) to a second Haversian canal (note the concentric bone lamellæ around the canal). The Volkmann's canal then turns right (across bottom of picture). By such a route blood vessels and nerves supply bone tissue.

In *lamellar bone* the lamellæ are not arranged in small concentric circles. Lamellar bone makes up the outside surface of most bones, the lamellæ following the surface, or circumference, of the bone (Figs. 56, 57). In this location the lamellar bone is sometimes given the additional names of *circumferential bone*, or *subperiosteal bone* (subperiosteal = beneath the periosteum). Lamellar bone also often makes up the surfaces of the trabeculæ of trabecular bone; and in this location it may be called *sub-endosteal bone* (beneath the endosteum). Both patterns of arrangement of lamellæ, *i.e.*, Haversian system bone and lamellar bone, are found in all mature bone tissue.

Regardless of the arrangement of bone lamellæ, all bone tissue contains osteocytes which lie in lacunæ and connect through canaliculi. This system of connected bone cells (Fig. 58) is the means by which nutrients are distributed throughout the bone tissue. In an Haversian system some of the canaliculi open into the Haversian canal, providing a pathway by which nutrients from the blood vessels contained in the canal may reach the osteocytes of the Haversian system.

Bone is a very vascular tissue; it contains many blood vessels. Arteries and veins enter and leave a bone in various places both from the outside surface and from the bone marrow cavity. The canals in a bone through

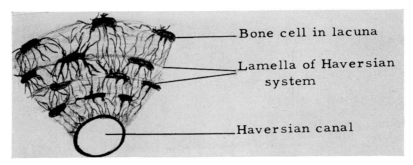

Bone cell in lacuna

Lamella of Haversian system

Haversian canal

FIGURE 58.—Diagrammatic drawing of a sector of an Haversian system cut in cross section. (As seen under high power magnification.)

which blood vessels pass into the bone tissue from the outside of the organ or from the bone marrow cavity are called *Volkmann's canals* (Figs. 56 and 57). Branches of the blood vessels contained in Volkmann's canals enter the smaller Haversian canals.

It seems remarkable that blood vessels should enter bones and be distributed throughout bones in the way that they are; but actually, in the embryonic development of the body, the larger blood vessels are formed and are in place before bone formation begins. As bone is formed it simply surrounds and encloses any blood vessels located in the area. Therefore we find blood vessels entering and leaving bones at various points.

Bone marrow, which occupies the centers of bones in the spaces around the trabeculæ, is a soft tissue (Figs. 55 and 65). There are two types of bone marrow: (1) *red marrow*, which is found in most of the bones of young individuals and has the function of producing red and white blood cells; and (2) *yellow marrow* (fat marrow), which does not have a blood-forming function. In adults most red marrow becomes converted into yellow marrow. Only certain locations in the adult skeleton retain the red type of marrow which continues to perform the function of hemopoiesis (hemo = blood; poiesis = creation).

Periosteum and Endosteum

On the outside surface a bone is covered by a more or less tough connective tissue membrane called the *periosteum*. A thinner, more delicate connective tissue membrane, called the *endosteum*, covers the inner surface of compact bone and the trabeculæ in the bone marrow cavity, and lines the Haversian canals and the Volkmann's canals. These two membranes, the periosteum and the endosteum, function both in the formation and in the resorption of bone tissue.

The periodontal ligament which surrounds the root of a tooth and separates it from the bone of the tooth socket is a specialized periosteum. It functions on one side in the formation and resorption of the bone comprising the tooth socket and on the other side in the formation and resorption of the cementum covering the tooth root.

Growth of Bone

Bone growth includes both *bone formation* and *bone resorption*.

Bone formation is the conversion of relatively unspecialized connective tissue into bone matrix and bone cells, and the subsequent calcification of the bone matrix. Bone matrix is composed of two kinds of intercellular substance: fibrous and amorphous. It arises as a result of a chemical change which takes place in the fibrous and amorphous intercellular substances of unspecialized connective tissue. The bone cells are certain cells of this same connective tissue which are entrapped in the forming bone matrix. In a growing bone the connective tissue which forms the new bone is the periosteum, or the endosteum, as the case may be, depending on whether the new bone is being added to the outside or to the inside of the organ. The intercellular substance of the part of the periosteum (or endosteum) which lies against the bone surface is chemically changed into bone matrix. Some of the cells of the periosteum (or endosteum) next to the bone surface become specialized and are called *osteoblasts* (osteo = bone; blast = germ) (Figs. 60 and 61). As the new bone matrix is formed, some of these osteoblasts become surrounded by it and so become cells of the bone tissue, *osteocytes*. Because the osteoblasts in the periosteum (or endosteum) are not completely isolated cells but have their cytoplasm connected by numerous thin projections, the osteocytes likewise are not isolated cells but have their cytoplasm connected by the same thin projections (Fig. 58). The spaces in the bone matrix occupied by the osteocytes are the lacunæ; and the spaces occupied by the numerous cytoplasmic connections are the canaliculi.

In the embryonic development of certain bones the formation of bone tissue is preceded by the formation of a cartilage structure which resembles in shape the bone that is to be formed and which serves as a pattern for the future bone. This cartilage predecessor of the bone calcifies and then is gradually removed by resorption. As the calcified cartilage is resorbed, bone tissue is formed to replace it. Bones which arise in this way, with a cartilage structure preceding the development of bone tissue, are said to be formed by *endochondral bone formation*. Examples of bones formed in this manner are the long bones of the arms and legs.

In the embryonic development of other bones, the bone tissue is formed without a preceding cartilage pattern, and these bones are said to be formed by *intramembranous bone formation* (Fig. 59). Examples of bones formed in this manner, with no preceding cartilage structure, are the mandible and the maxilla. The process of the conversion of unspecialized connective tissue into bone and the final microscopic structure of bone tissue are the same whether or not bone formation has been preceded by cartilage.

At first glance bone appears to be a permanent and unchanging tissue. Actually, bone is in a state of constant change. Bone tissue formation

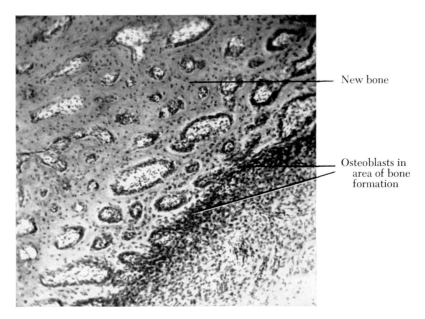

New bone

Osteoblasts in area of bone formation

FIGURE 59.—A photomicrograph of a section of forming bone in the area of the mandible in a kitten fetus. This is intramembranous bone formation. Osteoblasts are numerous. The connective tissue from which the bone is forming is in the lower right corner. (Medium power magnification.)

continues practically throughout the life of the bone, but the organ does not thereby become indefinitely heavier and greater in mass. The density and size of a bone are limited by the fact that the formation of bone tissue in one place is compensated for by the resorption of bone tissue in another.

Bone resorption is the removal of both the mineral materials and the organic matrix of bone. Resorption of bone should not be confused with decalcification of bone (or other hard tissues) such as occurs when the tissue is removed from the body and taken to the laboratory to be placed in a weak acid solution. In this laboratory procedure, called decalcification, the mineral material is removed and the organic material remains. In bone resorption, the organic matrix and the mineral material are both removed, and nothing of the bone remains.

Bone resorption occurs just beneath the periosteum or endosteum. A specialized type of cell called an *osteoclast* (clast = break) is associated with the resorption of bone tissue (Fig. 62). Osteoclasts are multinucleated cells (contain more than one nucleus), the nuclei ranging from 2 or 3 to a dozen or more in a single cell. Osteoclasts, like osteoblasts, originate from the cells of the periosteum or endosteum. Their function is not clearly understood, but their presence, seen microscopically, is an indication that bone resorption was occurring in this tissue (Figs. 60, 61).

Bone formation and bone resorption are processes that occur intermittently in all bones throughout the life of the individual. The intra-

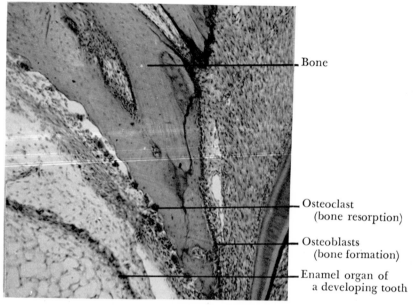

FIGURE 60.—A photomicrograph of a small area of kitten mandible in the region of developing teeth. The large triangular piece of bone shows bone resorption on one side (*left*) and bone formation on the other side (*right*). In the area of bone resorption are a large number of osteoclasts on the bone surface. Resorption in this area is probably due to the presence of a developing tooth, the enamel organ of which is seen in the lower left. On the right side of the triangular bone the presence of numerous, closely packed osteoblasts on the bone surface are associated with formation of bone tissue in this area. (Low power magnification.)

membranous bone (Fig. 59) and the endochondral bone that form in the early development of the individual are gradually resorbed and are replaced by mature bone. With growth and function the mature bone undergoes an endless process of resorption in one place and apposition (formation) in another. Haversian systems are partially or wholly resorbed and then replaced by other Haversian systems or by lamellar bone. Lamellar bone on the surface of a bone is resorbed and replaced by new Haversian system bone or by new lamellar bone. This turnover is rapid during the growth of the individual, and occurs more slowly later in life. After full individual growth is attained, however, the processes of bone change may occur rapidly in places where function or trauma stimulate resorption or apposition.

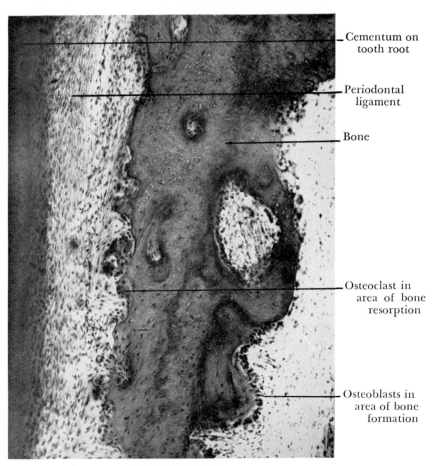

Cementum on tooth root

Periodontal ligament

Bone

Osteoclast in area of bone resorption

Osteoblasts in area of bone formation

FIGURE 61.—A photomicrograph of an area of tooth root, periodontal ligament, and alveolar bone (lamina dura). This was a tooth not in function: notice the lack of orientation of periodontal ligament fibers. There is bone resorption on the bone surface next to the periodontal ligament. Notice the osteoclasts. On the other surface of the bone (to the right) the presence of osteoblasts indicates bone formation. (Medium power magnification.)

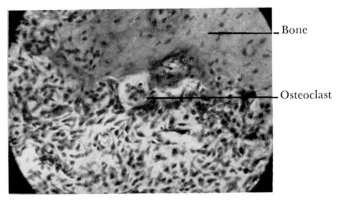

Bone

Osteoclast

FIGURE 62.—A photomicrograph (high power magnification) of osteoclasts in the area of bone development of a kitten mandible. Bone development of course includes bone resorption as well as bone formation and the presence of osteoclasts indicates that this is an area of resorption. Bone is at the top of the picture; bone-forming connective tissue is at the bottom. The osteoclast in the center of the picture distinctly shows the presence of nine nuclei.

Bone formation and bone resorption are taking place almost continuously in some areas of the bone tissue that surrounds the teeth. They occur in response to certain stimuli. In the tooth socket the stimuli which govern bone formation and bone resorption are: (1) tension (pull) on the periodontal ligament fibers attached to the bone, and (2) pressure on the periodontal ligament and on the bone. Tension on the periodontal ligament fibers induces bone formation; pressure induces bone resorption.

THE ALVEOLAR PROCESS

The *alveolar process* is defined as that part of the mandible and maxillæ which surrounds and supports the teeth (Fig. 63). The alveolar process

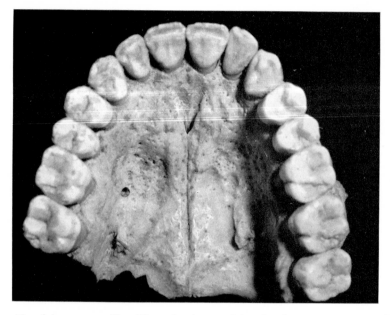

FIGURE 63.—A human maxilla. The palatal part of the alveolar process merges without a distinct line into the bone of the palate. The alveolar process extending between the teeth is seen clearly. The alveolar crest is the edge of the alveolar process around the cervix of the tooth. Notice the attrition of the incisal edges of the anterior teeth.

supports the tooth roots on the facial and on the palatal and lingual sides; it extends between the teeth, separating them on the mesial and distal sides; and it extends into the furcation of the roots of multirooted teeth (Figs. 55, 65). The occlusal border of the alveolar process, located near the cervix of the tooth, is referred to as the *alveolar crest*.

The alveolar process may be described as being composed of the *lamina dura* and the *supporting bone*. The lamina dura is the bone of the wall of the tooth socket. The supporting bone is made up of (1) the *cortical bone*, which is the outside wall of the mandible and the maxillæ and (2) the *trabecular bone* which is located between the lamina dura and the cortical bone in many areas (Figs. 55, 63, 64, 65, 73). In some areas the alveolar

Maxillary third molar

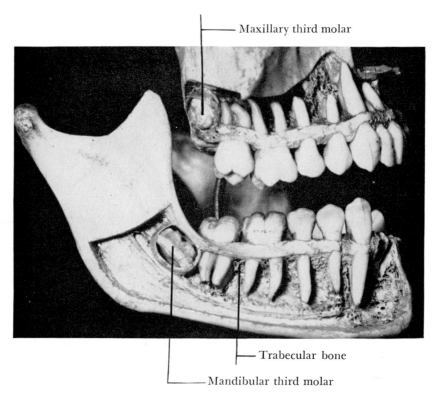

Trabecular bone

Mandibular third molar

FIGURE 64.—A human maxilla and mandible with the facial parts of the alveolar process removed excepting near the cervical border. In the mandible some trabecular bone remains among the tooth roots. Notice the location and position of the developing mandibular and maxillary third molars. (Chapters 11 and 12). The crown of the mandibular third molar is nearly completed in the ramus of the mandible. Its occlusal surface is directed mesially and occlusally. It is surrounded by a bony crypt. The maxillary third molar is directed buccally and distally.

FIGURE 65.—Diagrammatic drawing of a section of a human mandible bearing an isolated first molar tooth, cut mesiodistally. 1. Pulp horn. 2. Gingival fibers of periodontal ligament. 3. Bone of interradicular septum (between the roots). 4. Cortical bone on ridge of mandible. 5. Lamina dura bone near apex of distal root. 6. Cross section small blood vessel. 7. Fat marrow. 8. Trabecular bone scattered throughout bone marrow cavity. 9. Longitudinal section blood vessel. 10. Inferior alveolar nerve. 11. Cortical bone on inferior surface of mandible. *A*, *B*, *C*, and *D* indicate different areas of the periodontal ligament. *A*, the periodontal ligament on the mesial side of the mesial root; and *B*, the periodontal ligament on the mesial side of the distal root. At both *A* and *B* the principal fibers have a wavy appearance and there is evidence of resorption of the lamina dura bone. *C*, the periodontal ligament on the distal side of the mesial root; and *D*, the periodontal ligament on the distal side of the distal root. At *C* and *D* the principal fibers are stretched and there is no evidence of resorption of the lamina dura. It may be inferred that this tooth was undergoing a slight movement in a mesial direction: the slight pressure on the mesial side of each root resulted in relaxed periodontal ligament fibers and in bone resorption in the lamina dura. On the distal side of each root the fibers are straight and there is no evidence of bone resorption.

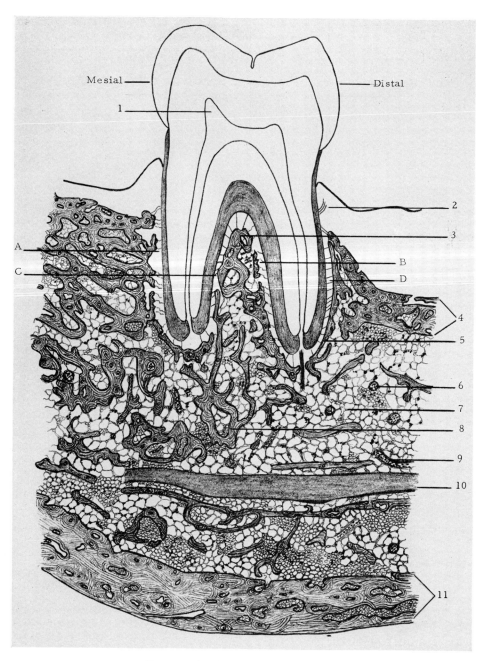

FIGURE 65.—*Legend on opposite page.*

process is thin and contains little or no trabecular bone: the lamina dura and the cortical plate are fused. This kind of thin alveolar process is found, among other places, on the facial surfaces of mandibular anterior teeth.

CLINICAL ASPECTS OF BONE REACTION IN THE ALVEOLAR PROCESS

The trabecular bone and the lamina dura which support a tooth react in different ways to changes in tooth function. When a tooth is in strong masticatory function, the trabecular bone in the alveolar process and the trabecular bone beneath the alveolus of the tooth are composed of numerous heavy bone trabeculæ. If the tooth is removed from function by loss of of opposing teeth, these supporting trabeculæ become less numerous and smaller. If the tooth in question is again placed in occlusion by the replacement of the lost teeth in the opposing arch, more trabecular bone will again form around the tooth which has resumed masticatory function.

The lamina dura, which comprises the tooth socket, does not respond by resorption to loss of masticatory function of the tooth. However, the lamina dura may respond by resorption to various stimuli such as trauma due to faulty occlusion, or periodontal disease, or pressures produced during orthodontic treatment, or pressures produced by mesial drift (See Chapter 12). Also, addition of bone tissue to the lamina dura at the base of the alveolus may be a factor in the continued occlusal movement of a tooth as attrition on the occlusal or incisal surface takes place. This addition to the lamina dura and the addition of cementum to the root, may partially compensate for loss of tooth length due to attrition.

Inflammation and swelling of the soft tissues around a tooth may result in damage to the periodontal ligament and resorption of the crest of the alveolar process (Figs. 55 and 76). The presence of calculus in the gingival sulcus has the potentiality to set off a series of events: The calculus produces inflammation and swelling of the adjacent soft tissues. This condition involves and damages the periodontal ligament fibers around the neck of the tooth. Damage to the periodontal ligament results in resorption of the bone to which the fibers are attached. Continued inflammation produces continued bone resorption. Eventually so much damage may be done to the periodontal ligament and to the lamina dura that removal of the tooth becomes necessary.

Good oral hygiene and prompt dental care will prevent such serious involvement because of the following consequential reactions: (1) Removal of the calculus may be expected to result in the elimination of the inflammation and swelling. (2) Elimination of the inflammation and swelling permits repair of the periodontal ligament. (3) At the same time there will be an arrest of the resorption of the bone of the alveolar crest. (4) Additional cementum may be produced on the tooth root in the affected area with an accompanying reattachment of the previously damaged periodontal ligament. (5) Repair of some of the resorbed areas of the lamina dura may occur, and some bone construction may possibly take place on the alveolar crest. It is probable that the alveolar crest will occupy a position apical to that of the original position—that is, there will not be enough bone replacement on the alveolar crest to make it as high as it was originally.

Teeth are sometimes, either by accident or by design, subjected to pressures on the crown from a horizontal direction (Fig. 65). If the pressure is continued and is not so severe as to damage the periodontal ligament, it will produce an adaptive response in the lamina dura. On the side of the tooth socket toward which the tooth is pushed the periodontal ligament and the lamina dura are subjected to pressures, and bone resorption occurs. On the side of the tooth socket away from which the tooth is pulled the periodontal ligament fibers are subjected to tension, and additional bone of the lamina dura is formed. The result of this bone resorption and bone formation is a change in the location of the tooth socket and also, of course, in the location of the tooth.

Such a change in the position of a tooth may be a result of a change in occlusal pressures. Or it may be a consequence of treatment applied by the orthodontist to improve unsatisfactory tooth alignment. The orthodontist places appliances on a patient's teeth and adjusts them at intervals so that proper pressures and tensions are maintained. The teeth being treated actually change location in the mouth. The success of this treatment is due to three factors: (1) Bone is resorbed more easily than cementum. (2) The area of the lamina dura toward which the tooth is moved is resorbed. (3) The area of the lamina dura away from which the tooth is moved is built up.

9

The Oral Mucous Membrane and the Salivary Glands

MUCOUS MEMBRANES

DEFINITION

A mucous membrane is the lining of a body cavity that opens to the outside of the body. Some examples of mucous membranes are found in the oral cavity, the nasal cavity and sinuses, the trachea, the stomach and intestines, the urinary bladder, the uterus.

HISTOLOGIC STRUCTURE OF MUCOUS MEMBRANES

Histologically a mucous membrane is a modified skin. It is made up of two layers: (1) a surface layer of *epithelial tissue* and (2) an underlying layer of *connective tissue*. Mucous membranes are structurally less thick and tough than the skin; and whereas the skin is kept slightly moist by secretions from oil glands and sweat glands which empty onto the surface, mucous membranes are kept very moist by secretions from mucous glands, serous glands, or other secretory cells which empty onto the surface. The epithelium of a mucous membrane is protective in function, and in some areas it is also secretory and absorptive in function. The connective tissue of a mucous membrane underlies the epithelium and contains blood vessels, nerves, and sometimes glands.

Mucous membranes in different parts of the body differ in a number of ways, and in each location their structure seems to be excellently suited to perform the functions required. In places where the mucous membrane is normally protected from wear and tear it is very thin and delicate, while in areas which are subjected to functional friction it is thicker and resistant to injury.

Protected cavities such as the nasal cavity, the stomach, and the intestines are lined by delicate types of mucous membranes. *In the nasal cavity* the epithelial part of the mucous membrane is composed of pseudostratified columnar cells (Fig. 13D). Many of these columnar cells have *cilia*—tiny hair-like projections—on their exposed ends, while others, called *goblet cells*, secrete mucus which keeps the surface of the mucosa moist. The connective tissue part of the nasal mucous membrane is likewise thin and delicate, and contains nerves and blood vessels, and mucous and serous glands which open onto the surface of the mucosa. This moist, ciliated mucous membrane of the nasal passage functions as a dirt-catcher and prevents the dust which is inhaled with the air from reaching the lungs.

Lining the stomach is a mucous membrane which is somewhat thicker than that of the nasal cavity, and which is arranged in many folds and wrinkles. The epithelium of the stomach mucosa is made up of simple columnar cells which are without cilia and which have a secretory function. The underlying connective tissue contains many glands.

In many respects resembling the stomach mucosa, the *mucosa of the small intestine* has an epithelium composed of simple columnar cells some of which are goblet cells that secrete mucus and others of which have the function of absorbing food materials from the intestine. The connective tissue contains many glands.

Contrasted with these protected, delicate mucous membranes of the nasal cavity, the stomach, and the intestines, is the more sturdy mucosa which *lines the oral cavity*. The lining of the mouth is constantly subjected to rubbing and scraping, not only by the process of mastication of food, but also by the presence of the teeth in the mouth; and here again the construction of the mucous membrane is suited to its usage.

THE ORAL MUCOUS MEMBRANE

HISTOLOGIC STRUCTURE OF ORAL MUCOUS MEMBRANE

The mucous membrane lining the mouth is heavier and more resistant to injury than the mucous membranes of more protected cavities. Its histologic structure enables the oral mucosa to withstand the wear and tear of ordinary oral function and to resist bacterial infection. Like all mucous membranes, the oral mucosa is composed of a combination of epithelial tissue and connective tissue.

The *epithelial portion of the oral mucosa* is stratified squamous in character—that is, the epithelial cells are mostly flat in shape and are several layers deep. As in all stratified squamous epithelium, the basal layer of epithelial cells, which rests upon the connective tissue, is composed of cuboidal rather than flat cells; and it is in this basal layer that most of the cell division takes place. As new epithelial cells are produced by mitosis in the basal layer, some of the basal cells and the cells superficial to them are forced outward and eventually they reach the surface.

Different things happen to these surface epithelial cells in different parts of the mouth. In areas of the mouth where the mucosa is relatively protected, such as on the inside of the cheeks and lips and on the under side of the tongue, the surface epithelial cells are sloughed off into the saliva as new epithelial cells are produced in the basal layer (Fig. 14). A scraping from the inside of the cheeks spread onto a glass slide and examined under the microscope will be seen to contain squamous epithelial cells.

In some other parts of the mouth where the oral mucosa is subject to considerable wear and tear, such as the hard palate and the gingiva, the surface epithelial cells are not sloughed off (Fig. 66). Instead, they loose their nuclei and their cell boundaries and form a noncellular, tough, protective layer on the surface of the stratified squamous epithelial cells. This tough layer is called the *keratin layer*, and epithelium on which such a layer occurs is called *keratinized epithelium*. The keratin layer wears with use, of course, but it is continuously replaced by the aging cells beneath it.

The *connective tissue portion of the oral mucosa* is composed chiefly of fibrous connective tissue in which are blood vessels and nerves. It is separated from the overlying stratified squamous epithelium by a thin basement membrane. In most places the junction between the connective tissue and the epithelium is an irregular boundary with projections of connective tissue extending like fingers up into the epithelium, but not reaching the surface. In some areas of the oral mucosa these projections

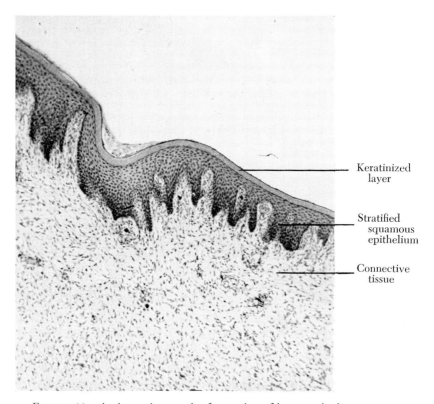

Keratinized layer

Stratified squamous epithelium

Connective tissue

FIGURE 66.—A photomicrograph of a section of human gingiva.
(As seen under low power magnification.)

are characteristically much longer and more numerous than in other areas (Figs. 14 and 66). This irregularity of contact surfaces between the two tissues serves to increase the area from which the epithelium can receive nourishment from the underlying connective tissue.

The connective tissue of the oral mucosa varies in thickness in different parts of the mouth; and it also varies in the nature of its attachment to the underlying tissue. In some areas of the mouth the connective tissue of the oral mucosa is attached directly to underlying bone, as in the part of the gingiva which is attached to the periosteum of the alveolar process. In other areas of the mouth the connective tissue of the oral mucosa rests upon a looser type of connective tissue called the *submucosa*, which con-

tains larger bood vessels, nerves, glands, and fat tissue. Such an attachment of oral mucosa to submucosa is seen in the cheek. The character of
the submucosa varies in different parts of the mouth, and its nature helps
to determine the character of the mucosa which it supports.

For convenience in discussion an attempt has been made to classify
the different areas of oral mucosa. The classification divides the oral
mucosa into three categories: (1) the *masticatory mucosa*, (2) the *lining
mucosa*, and (3) the *specialized mucosa*. If you will carefully examine
someone's mouth and observe the mucosa in different places, such a division
will seem logical.

Masticatory mucosa

> Gingiva
> Hard palate

Lining mucosa

> Lips and cheeks
> Floor of mouth
> Under side of tongue
> Soft palate
> Alveolar mucosa

Specialized mucosa

> Dorsum of tongue

The *masticatory mucosa* is the name given to the mucous membrane of
the *gingiva* and of the *hard palate*. These are the areas of the oral mucosa
most used during the mastication of food. The epithelium of the masticatory mucosa is usually keratinized.

Looking into a person's mouth you will see that the necks of the teeth
and the bone in which the teeth are set are covered with a firm mucous
membrane which fits close around the teeth and is tightly attached to the
bone. This part of the oral mucosa is called the *gingiva* (Fig. 71). The
gingiva is usually keratinized, is firm, and has a stippled appearance.
Excepting for a narrow zone around the necks of the teeth the gingival
mucosa is attached firmly to the underlying tissue. If you will examine
the facial side of the upper and lower jaws, you will notice that several
millimeters rootward from the margin of the gingiva there is a scalloped
line which divides the gingival mucosa from the alveolar mucosa (Fig. 71).
The alveolar mucosa may be distinguished from the gingiva because it is
redder, shiny, and loose-fitting.

The mucosa covering the *hard palate* is usually well keratinized. It is
attached directly to the bone of the roof of the mouth only in the area of
the *palatine raphe*, which is the anteroposterior elevation in the center of
the hard palate that you can feel with your tongue. On either side of the
palatine raphe the palatine mucosa has a submucosa between it and the
bone. In the anterior part the submucosa in the hard palate contains
much fat tissue, and in the posterior part it contains large salivary glands
of the mucous type. The ducts of these glands open onto the surface of
the palate mucosa. These small openings are not visible to the naked eye.

Notwithstanding the presence of the fat tissue and gland tissue in the
submucosa of the hard palate, the oral mucosa in this area is firmly

attached to the underlying bone structure. This is accomplished by strands of connective tissue which extend from the mucosa through the submucosa and attach firmly to the bone of the roof of the mouth.

Lining mucosa is located in those areas of the oral cavity where the mucous membrane might logically be regarded as functioning as a lining organ rather than as a masticatory organ. Such nonmasticatory areas are the inside of the cheeks and lips, the floor of the mouth and the under side of the tongue, the soft palate, and the alveolar mucosa. In none of these areas is the mucosa firmly attached to the underlying bone, and ordinarily the epithelium of these areas is not keratinized. In the cheeks, lips, and soft palate there is a thick submucosa which contains fat tissue and numerous salivary glands whose minute duct openings are scattered over the surface of the mucosa. In the cheek or lip mucosa you may occasionally see what appears to be a pea-sized bubble just beneath the surface.

FIGURE 67.—Drawing of a section of human tongue through fungiform and filiform papillæ. This fungiform papilla measured about 1 mm. in diameter. (As seen under high power magnification.)

This condition is due to a stoppage in one of these small salivary ducts which has resulted in an accumulation at this point of the secretion from a salivary gland. This bubble is called a *mucocele*.

If you will examine the cheek mucosa inside the corners of the mouth of several individuals you will often find an area which has a few, or numerous, small yellowish spots which are called *Fordyce's spots*. These spots are the openings onto the oral mucosa of sebaceous glands. Of course sebaceous glands are usually thought of as being restricted to the skin on the outside of the body. Their occurrence in this location of the oral cavity is not unusual, however, and is of no clinical significance. They probably occur here as a result of the narrowing of the wide embryonic mouth during the early development of the face—*i.e.*, in the fusion of the maxillary process and the mandibular process at either corner of the mouth some of these skin glands are entrapped in the oral mucosa at the line of union (Fig. 7).

Specialized mucosa is the term applied to the mucous membrane located on the dorsum (top side) of the tongue. The mucosa in this area is distinctly different from other oral mucosa. Examine someone's tongue and you will see that the mucosa of its upper surface is formed into innumerable small *papillæ*. These papillæ are of several kinds, different in size and shape, and some of them bear microscopic organs which supply the sense of taste.

Filiform papillæ (thread-like) cover the top surface of the tongue and give it a velvety appearance. The epithelium covering the tips of the

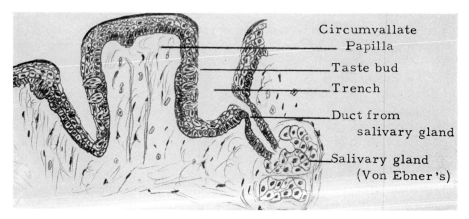

FIGURE 68.—Drawing of a section of a human tongue through a circumvallate papilla. This papilla measured about 1.5 mm. in diameter. (As seen under high power magnification.)

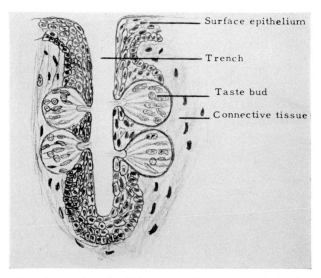

FIGURE 69.—Drawing of a section of rabbit tongue showing taste buds along the wall of a trench surrounding a papilla. (As seen under high power magnification.)

filiform papillæ is heavily keratinized (Fig. 67). In the human tongue the keratinization is not sufficient to impart the sandpaper-like quality you feel in the keratinized papillæ on a kitten's tongue if the kitten licks your hand.

Fungiform papillæ (mushroom-shaped) are larger and less numerous than the filiform. They are scattered among the filiform papillæ (Fig. 67).

Due to their thinner epithelium they appear redder in color than the fili-form papillæ. They may be clearly seen by careful examination of the tongue.

Foliate papillæ are located along the lateral borders of the posterior part of the tongue. In the human tongue these papillæ are not well developed.

Circumvallate papillæ can be seen well back on the tongue, located be-tween the body and the base of the tongue (Fig. 68). They are large, conspicuous structures, 8 to 10 in number, arranged in a V-shaped line with the point of the V directed toward the throat.

The fungiform, foliate, and circumvallate papillæ contain organs of taste. If a longitudinal section of a circumvallate papilla is examined with a microscope, there may be seen groups of specialized epithelial cells, which are called *taste buds*, located along the lateral surfaces of the papilla (Fig. 68). Figure 69 is a drawing of such taste buds seen in a section of rabbit tongue, where the details are more easily studied than in the human tongue. These are similar to human taste buds. At the bottom of the trench surrounding the human circumvallate papilla there are openings of ducts leading from salivary glands (Von Ebner's glands) which are located deep in the tongue. The saliva from these glands floods the trench around the circumvallate papilla and serves as a solvent for food substances. When these food substances in solution come in contact with the taste buds the individual experiences a sensation of taste.

THE SALIVARY GLANDS

HISTOLOGY AND FUNCTION OF SALIVARY GLANDS

Salivary glands produce a colorless, slightly sticky fluid called *saliva* which is discharged into the oral cavity through ducts that open onto the surface of the oral mucosa.

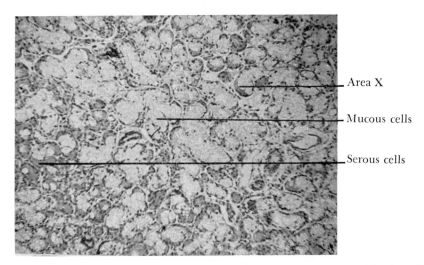

FIGURE 70.—A section of a human sublingual gland. Medium power magnification. Most of the gland cells are of the mucous type. Some serous cells (darker stain) form a cap around a group of mucous cells (Area X).

In embryonic development the salivary glands are formed from the epithelium that lines the early oral cavity.   In certain areas cells of the embryonic oral epithelium grow downward into the underlying connective tissue, and as they multiply the epithelial cells of this downgrowth become modified and very specialized and form the salivary glands.   Some of the cells develop into the secretory cells of the glands, and others develop into the ducts of the glands.   The secretory cells secrete the saliva.   There are two types of salivary secretory cells: *serous cells* and *mucous cells* (Fig. 70).   Salivary glands are made up of one, or of the other, or of a combination of the two kinds of secretory cells plus the ducts which connect them.   The secreted product of serous cells contains an enzyme called amylase (ptyalin) which contributes to the breakdown of carbohydrates.   The secreted product of the mucous cells is mucin which acts as a lubricant to the oral cavity.   Besides these substances the salivary glands secrete other materials among which are proteins and salts which act as buffers and prevent the saliva from becoming suddenly acid or alkaline.   Also, saliva contains some antibacterial factor which inhibits the growth of some bacteria.   In addition to these products of the salivary glands saliva which has been lying in the mouth contains various sorts of debris such as epithelial cells sloughed off the oral mucosa, degenerating white blood cells, and bacteria.

The total amount of saliva produced by the salivary glands varies greatly in different individuals, but an approximate amount is about 3 pints a day.

The functions of saliva may be enumerated as follows: (1) it assists in the mastication of food; (2) it serves as a solvent; (3) it contributes to the digestion of carbohydrates; (4) it lubricates food and oral tissues; (5) it acts as a buffer; (6) it cleanses the mouth by flushing out debris; (7) it acts to inhibit the growth of some bacteria.

DISTRIBUTION OF SALIVARY GLANDS

The salivary glands may be described in two groups: (A) the *major salivary glands*, and (B) the *minor salivary glands*.   The major salivary glands are (1) the *parotid*, (2) the *submandibular (submaxillary)*, and (3) the *sublingual*.   The minor salivary glands vary in size and are widely distributed beneath the oral mucous membrane.

The *major salivary glands* are, of course, paired structures.   The *parotid glands* are flattened organs located under the skin of the face in front of and below each ear.   They are the largest of the salivary glands, and in adult human beings their secretory cells are all serous in type.   The parotid gland is the gland involved in epidemic parotitis, commonly known as mumps.   The main duct of each parotid gland, the *parotid duct (Stensen's duct)*, opens into the oral cavity on the wall of either cheek opposite the second maxillary molar tooth.   If the tongue is passed over this area a small prominence may be felt at the point where the duct opens into the mouth.

The *submandibular glands* are located beneath the posterior part of the tongue.   They lie in a depression on the inner surface of either side of the mandible just anterior to the angle of the jaw. The secretory cells which make up these glands are a combination of serous and mucous cells, the serous being the more numerous. The secreted product of these glands is a mixture of serous and mucous substances. The main ducts which carry the products of the submandibular glands to the oral cavity open into the mouth beneath the tongue, one on either side of the center line. You can see the openings easily as two small prominences in this area. These ducts are known as the *submandibular ducts (Wharton's ducts)*.

The *sublingual glands* are located beneath the mucosa in the floor of the mouth anterior to the submandibular glands. They are composed of a mixture of serous and mucous types of cells, but are predominantly mucous in character (Fig. 70). The main ducts which carry the products of this pair of glands are several in number, and all open beneath the tongue. Some open along the folds of tissue which are seen on either side of the floor of the mouth, while others join the submandibular ducts and share the same openings. Examine carefully the area under the tongue in a human mouth.

The *minor salivary glands* may be described according to their location in the oral cavity. Beneath the mucous membrane of the cheeks and lips are numerous small glands which are a mixture of mucous and serous secretory cells, the mucous cells being the more numerous. The minute duct openings of these small glands are scattered over the surface of the cheek and lip mucosa. Larger salivary glands made up entirely of mucous cells lie beneath the mucous membrane of the roof of the mouth and have minute duct openings distributed over the entire surface of the hard and soft palate. The tongue has glands in its anterior part which are mixed in character (contain both serous and mucous cells). In the posterior part of the tongue are the pure serous *Von Ebner's glands* whose ducts empty into the trenches of the circumvallate papillæ. There are also pure mucous glands in the root of the tongue.

10

The Gingiva

LOCATION

The gingiva is that part of the oral mucosa that is firmly attached to the alveolar process and to the cervical parts of the teeth and which surrounds the cervices of the teeth.

The gingiva on the facial side of the maxillæ and mandible in the premolar and molar regions is called the *buccal gingiva,* and in the incisor and canine regions the *labial gingiva.* The gingiva on the inside of the mandibular arch is called the *lingual gingiva,* and on the inside of the maxillary arch, the *palatal gingiva.*

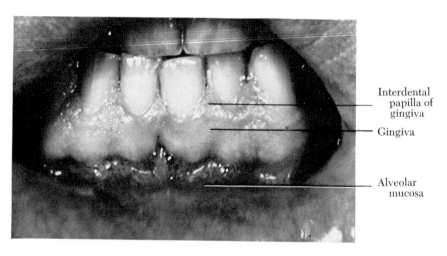

Interdental
papilla of
gingiva

Gingiva

Alveolar
mucosa

FIGURE 71.—Clinical photograph of mandibular anterior teeth with associated gingiva and alveolar mucosa. The subject was twenty years old. Notice the difference in color of the gingiva and the alveolar mucosa; the stippled texture of the gingiva; the interdental papillæ.

CLINICAL APPEARANCE

To study the clinical appearance of the gingiva stand before a mirror or use a classmate for a subject. Pull out and down on the lower lip. Below the crowns of the mandibular anterior teeth you will see that the oral mucous membrane is firm and has a stippled or finely pitted appearance. This is gingiva (Fig. 71). In people who have fair skins the color of the gingiva is a slightly grayish pink. In dark complexioned individuals the gingiva frequently is either spotted with brown or is fairly even grayish brown all over due to a pigment which occurs in some of the cells of the epithelium. Four or five millimeters below its cervical margin the gingiva ends in a scalloped line and the oral mucosa below this line is red, shiny, and loosely attached to the underlying tissue. Examine also the gingiva above the maxillary anterior teeth, and the gingiva on the buccal side of the mandibular and maxillary posterior teeth. The color and surface texture here are the same as in the anterior region, and a scalloped line marks the apical border.

Now examine the lingual side of the mandibular arch. The gingiva is firmly attached to the underlying hard tissue, while the oral mucosa beneath the tongue is loose, shiny, and redder in color than the gingiva.

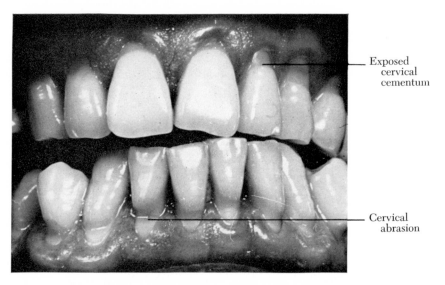

Exposed
cervical
cementum

Cervical
abrasion

FIGURE 72.—Clinical photograph of maxillary and mandibular anterior teeth with associated gingiva. The subject was sixty years old. Notice the stippled gingiva; the position of the interdental papillæ; the exposed but undamaged cementum on the left maxillary lateral incisor and on the right maxillary central incisor. Notice the exposed and deeply cut cementum on the mandibular anterior teeth. This is cervical abrasion.

Examine the palatal side of the maxillary arch. In the maxilla the palatal gingiva blends without a distinct line into the oral mucosa of the hard palate.

Look again at the facial surfaces of the mandibular and maxillary arches. The shape of the incisal (or occlusal) border of the gingiva depends largely on the age of the individual. In a very young person the gingiva extends between the teeth in a triangular *interdental papilla*, reaching as far occlusally or incisally between the teeth as the contact areas; and on the facial and lingual surfaces of the teeth the gingiva will cover the cervical part of the enamel of the tooth crown. In this young person the *clinical crown* of the tooth (the part exposed in the oral cavity) is smaller than the *anatomic crown* of the tooth (the part that has an enamel surface).

In a person who is near thirty years of age the points of the interdental papillæ do not extend to the contact areas, and most or all of the tooth enamel probably is uncovered: the clinical crown and the anatomic crown are often about the same.

Now examine a person fifty or sixty years old and compare what you see here with what you saw in the very young person and in the younger adult. In the middle aged or older person you will probably find that not only do the interdental papillæ fail to fill the spaces that exist between the teeth cervical to the contact areas (the interproximal spaces), but on some or all surfaces of the teeth cementum can be seen around the cervix (Fig. 72). The gingival margin in this older person is located so far rootward that some of the root cementum is exposed in the oral cavity, and the clinical crown of the tooth is larger than the anatomic crown.

This age change in the position of the gingiva on the tooth is a condition that is to be expected, just as it is expected that with age hair will become gray and skin will become wrinkled. Of course, diseases of the tissues around the teeth may produce pathologic changes with gingival recession at any age. What we are discussing here are usual and expected age changes.

Histologic Structure

Like all other mucous membranes the gingiva is composed of connective tissue and epithelial tissue. The connective tissue is of the fibrous type, while the epithelial tissue, which is of course on the surface, is stratified squamous in character and is usually keratinized (Fig. 66). This keratinization causes the color of the gingiva to be grayish pink rather than red if it is not pigmented, or grayish brown rather than reddish brown if pigmentation is present; and the finger-shaped projections of the connective tissue into the epithelium probably produce the pitted condition of the surface of the epithelium in some places. The gingiva does not have a submucosa, but rests directly on the underlying hard tissue; and ordinarily the gingiva contains no salivary glands.

The Gingival Sulcus

The part of the gingiva that covers the alveolar process is firmly attached to that bone structure. Occlusal to the crest of the alveolar process the gingiva for a short space is firmly attached to the tooth surface by the gingival fibers of the periodontal ligament (Fig. 73). Occlusal to the portion of the gingiva which is attached to the tooth surface there is a border of gingiva surrounding the tooth which is not attached to the tooth. This unattached part of the gingiva is called the *free gingiva*. Often the free gingiva fits so snugly to the surface of the tooth that there is only a potential space, rather than an actual space, between the tooth surface and the free gingiva. Regardless of whether the space between the tooth and the free gingiva is actual or only potential, it is called the *gingival sulcus*. The gingival sulcus could be roughly described as a ditch, or a potential ditch, extending all around the tooth between the tooth surface and the cervical border of the gingiva.

The structure of the tissue associated with the gingival sulcus is important. To simplify description, let us suppose that a small instrument is inserted into the gingival sulcus so that an actual space is created between the tooth and the free gingiva (Observe Fig. 73). The inner wall of this space is of course the surface of the tooth. The outer wall of the space is the free gingiva, the inner surface of which is composed of stratified squamous epithelium. This epithelium is called the *epithelium of the gingival sulcus,* and it is continuous over the gingival margin with the stratified squamous epithelium which makes up the outside surface of the gingiva.

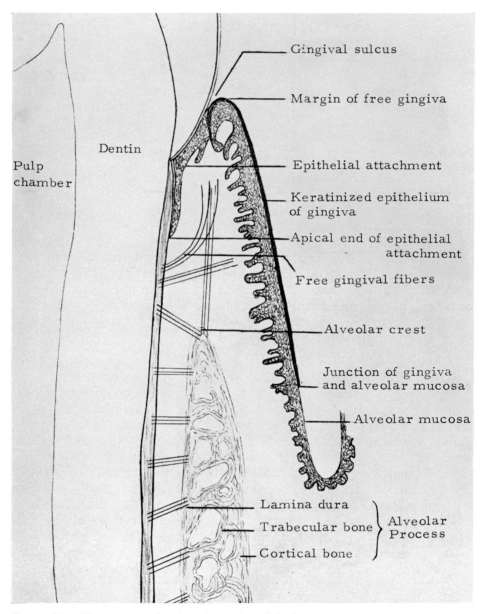

FIGURE 73.—Diagrammatic drawing of a section of the buccal cervical area of a mandibular molar tooth cut buccolingually.

To what depth our instrument may be inserted between the tooth and the gingiva without tearing loose gingival tissue which is actually attached to the tooth surface is a matter about which there is a surprising difference of opinion. There exists a question among oral histologists whether, around the partially erupted tooth of a young person, the gingival tissue which covers the cervical part of the tooth crown is merely fitted snugly to the enamel surface or whether it is in some way attached to the enamel surface. If the gingival tissue is not attached to the enamel, the bottom of the gingival sulcus is always at least as deep as the line of the cemento-enamel junction. If, on the other hand, in a partially erupted tooth the gingival tissue which covers the cervical part of the crown *is* attached to the enamel which underlies it, the gingival sulcus may be very shallow. A number of studies have been made on this problem but the findings have been contradictory. Undoubtedly an answer will eventually be found which will be acceptable to all oral histologists.

THE EPITHELIAL ATTACHMENT

In young individuals the stratified squamous epithelium of the gingival sulcus, which is adjacent to the cervical part of the tooth crown, ends at the cementoenamel junction (Figs. 74C and D). As tooth eruption progresses the gingiva gradually moves rootward uncovering the crown, and at its apical border the stratified squamous epithelium which lines the gingival sulcus grows rootward from the cementoenamel junction along the root of the tooth (Figs. 74E, F, G). In this way the epithelium which covers the crown becomes extended onto the cementum of the root. This epithelium which grows onto the cementum is the *epithelial attachment*. It is scarcely worth the query whether the term epithelial attachment should be applied only to the epithelium covering the cementum, or whether it should be applied to the epithelium covering both the cementum and the enamel. The answer to this question of definition rests upon the answer to the question of whether or not this epithelium is attached to the enamel.

With age the gingiva continues slowly to move rootward from the crown of the tooth, and the epithelial attachment continues slowly to grow apically on the cementum. This process is partly a consequence of the slow occlusal tooth movement which seems to occur throughout the life of the tooth. Chiefly, however, this apical growth of the epithelium seems to take place independent of occlusal tooth movement and is referred to as the *rootward migration of the epithelial attachment*. This is a natural aging process and as such is not accompanied by inflammation. As aging continues the gingiva recedes to the point where the tooth crown is completely uncovered and exposed to the oral cavity (Fig. 74F). After this, continued gingival recession exposes cervical cementum and places the epithelial attachment considerably apical to the cementoenamel junction (Fig. 74G, H, I). When the cementum is exposed, the bottom of the gingival sulcus is of course somewhere on the tooth root, but it is not necessarily at the same level on all of the teeth in a mouth nor even on all sides of the same tooth. In a healthy mouth the gingival sulcus under these conditions is ordinarily shallow.

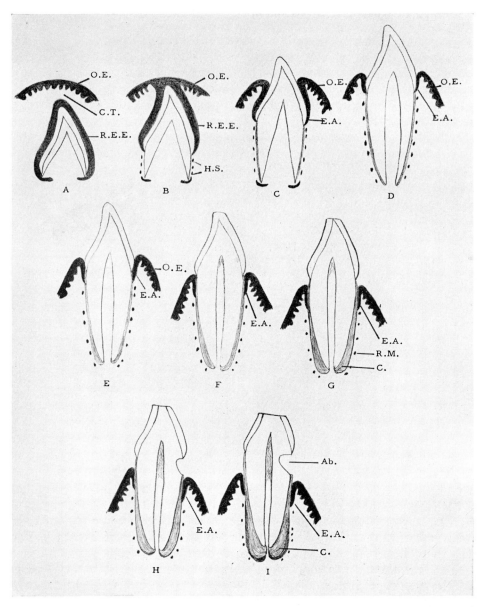

Figure 74.—*O.E.*—oral epithelium; *C.T.*—connective tissue; *R.E.E.*—reduced enamel epithelium; *H.S.*—Hertwig's sheath; *E.A.*—epithelial attachment; *R.M.*—rests of Malassez; *C*—cementum; *Ab.*—abrasion.

Diagrammatic illustration of the process of root formation, tooth eruption, the rootward migration of the epithelial attachment, cementum exposure, and cervical abrasion. (*A*) The reduced enamel epithelium covers the tooth crown and is separated from the oral epithelium by connective tissue. The root has not yet started to form. (*B*) Root formation has begun. The crown has moved incisally. The reduced enamel epithelium and the oral epithelium are in contact. (*C*) The root is longer. The incisal edge of the crown is exposed in the oral cavity. The reduced enamel epithelium (which is the remains of the enamel organ) is now continuous with the oral epithelium and is called the epithelial attachment. (*D*) The length of the root dentin is complete, and the crown has moved farther into the oral cavity. The epithelial attachment is still entirely on the enamel. The apical foramen is narrower. (*E*, *F*, *G*) The epithelial attachment grows onto the cementum at its apical border and separates from the tooth surface at its cervical border. Cementum becomes exposed. (*H*, *I*) Increased cementum exposure and improper use of an abrasive dentifrice have resulted in abrasion of cementum and dentin in the cervical area.

Exposure of cementum in older individuals is to be regarded as the usual and expected condition. Such cementum exposure is not infrequently seen to a slight degree on the maxillary canines, and sometimes on other teeth of persons less than thirty years old. After the age of thirty cementum exposure increases in frequency and extent. By forty years of age many individuals have cementum exposed on some areas of most of their teeth. By the age of sixty the amount of cementum exposure in some areas may often amount to 3 or 4 mm. (Fig. 72). It is unusual to find an individual of middle age with no cementum exposed on any teeth.

CLINICAL CONSIDERATIONS

The intactness of the epithelium of the gingival sulcus and epithelial attachment is important to good periodontal conditions. Since the gingival sulcus, despite the snug fit of the free gingiva to the tooth surface, is exposed to the saliva and bacteria of the oral cavity any damage to the epithelium of the gingival sulcus can result in damage to the underlying connective tissue. Connective tissue is not a covering tissue as is epithelial tissue, and it does not resist injury and bacterial invasion the way epithelial tissue does. Therefore, if damage to the epithelium of the gingival sulcus is accompanied by damage to the underlying connective tissue, the ensuing effects on the tissues in this area may be inflammation, swelling, damage to the periodontal ligament fibers, resorption of the bone of the alveolar process, loosening of the tooth, and perhaps finally the necessity for tooth removal.

The presence of calculus around the cervix of a tooth is often an important factor in periodontal disease (Fig. 46). The calculus damages the epithelium of the gingival sulcus and of the epithelial attachment. A series of consequential events follows: (1) There is inflammation of the connective tissue of the gingiva. (2) There is swelling. (3) There is damage to the periodontal ligament fibers, particularly the gingival, the transseptal, and the alveolar crest fibers. (4) There is resorption of the bone of the alveolar crest. (5) There is an increasing amount of cementum exposed in the cervical area of the tooth.

Figure 75 is a drawing of the cervical area of the lingual side of a maxillary molar tooth. The periodontium is in good condition: there is little or no inflammation in the gingiva; the epithelial attachment fits against the tooth; the periodontal ligament fibers are well oriented; and the alveolar crest shows no signs of resorption.

Figure 76 is a drawing of the cervical area of the buccal side of the same tooth. Here the presence of a mass of calculus has resulted in the formation of a gingival pocket. There has followed injury to the epithelium of the gingival sulcus, inflammation in the connective tissue, damage to the periodontal ligament fibers, and resorption of the alveolar crest and of the lamina dura. Continued irritation by the calculus will be accompanied by continued inflammation of the gingiva and continued bone resorption. Such pathosis sufficiently extended results in the loosening of the tooth.

Another important clinical problem is created by the presence in the mouth of exposed cervical cementum. When the extent of exposure of cervical cementum exceeds 1 mm. there frequently is found a condition known as *cervical abrasion*. Cervical abrasion is a wedge-shaped cut in the cervical cementum of a tooth. It is produced when the person uses an abrasive dentifrice and brushes his teeth with a cross-brushing stroke. The tooth enamel, due to its extreme hardness, is not affected by this

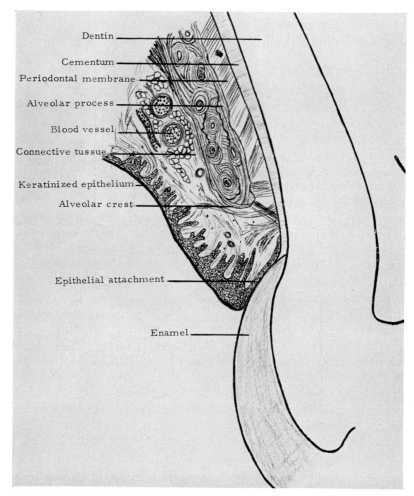

Dentin

Cementum

Periodontal membrane

Alveolar process

Blood vessel

Connective tussue

Keratinized epithelium

Alveolar crest

Epithelial attachment

Enamel

FIGURE 75.—Diagrammatic drawing of a longitudinal section cut faciolingually through a maxillary posterior tooth and the associated periodontal ligament, alveolar process, and gingiva. This is the lingual side of the tooth at the cervix. This area is free of inflammation. There is no bone resorption. The periodontal ligament (periodontal membrane) fibers are well oriented.

procedure, but the cementum is abraded. Cervical abrasion is seen in its most severe form in mouths that are consistently kept clean, and on the facial sides of the teeth where most vigorous brushing has been done. A study of the process of cervical abrasion has demonstrated that the use of cross-brushing technique with a very abrasive dentifrice can result in such an amount of abrasion that a maxillary canine tooth measuring 7 mm.

at the cervix may be cut half through in 7.6 years; that is, in that length of time the wedge of cervical abrasion can extend half way through the 7 mm. cervix. Such cervical abrasion is illustrated on the facial side of a mandibular incisor tooth in Figure 74*I*. Figure 72 is a clinical photograph showing cervical abrasion. Figure 77 is an extracted maxillary canine tooth showing deep cervical abrasion.

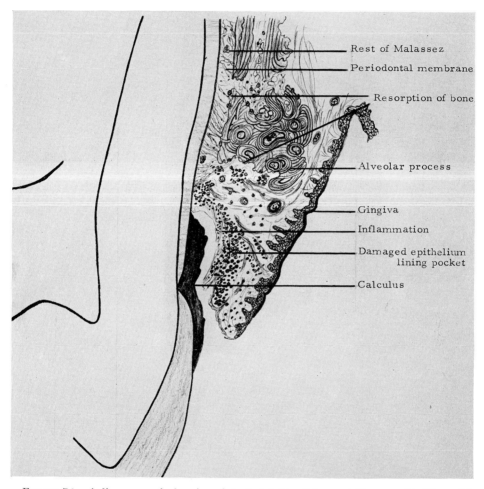

Rest of Malassez
Periodontal membrane
Resorption of bone
Alveolar process
Gingiva
Inflammation
Damaged epithelium lining pocket
Calculus

FIGURE 76.—A diagrammatic drawing of the facial side of the tooth illustrated in Figure 75. A large mass of calculus at the tooth cervix is responsible for the pathologic condition in this area. Here there is inflammation, destruction of the epithelial attachment, damaged periodontal ligament (periodontal membrane), and resorption of the alveolar crest and of the lamina dura.

Such information concerning cervical abrasion makes clear the importance of using proper tooth-brushing techniques and a dentifrice which does not contain an excessive amount of abrasive material. This is particularly important for those individuals in whom there has been considerable gingival recession leaving exposed to the oral cavity a relatively broad area of cementum.

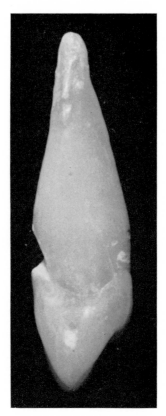

FIGURE 77.—Mesial surface of a maxillary canine tooth. There is deep abrasion of the cervical cementum on the facial surface. The enamel is not affected. Sclerotic dentin and secondary dentin (Figure 41) ordinarily form beneath such an area of abrasion.

11

Tooth Development

Before the human embryo is three weeks old the oral cavity is established. At the anterior end of the embryo the ectoderm has invaginated to meet the endoderm and has formed the primitive mouth and the buccopharyngeal membrane (Fig. 3). This membrane is located in approximately the position the palatine tonsils will later occupy. The primitive mouth is lined with ectoderm, beneath which is mesenchyme.* The ectoderm gives rise to the oral epithelium, and the mesenchyme gives rise to the underlying connective tissue.

The Beginning of Tooth Development

Not all teeth start development at the same time. The earliest sign of tooth development in the human embryo is found in the anterior mandibular region when the embryo is five to six weeks old. Soon after this, evidence of tooth development appears in the anterior maxillary region, and the process progresses posteriorly in both jaws.

The development of the teeth begins with the development of the *dental lamina*. The dental lamina is a narrow band of thickened oral epithelium (ectoderm) which extends along the occlusal borders of the mandible and maxillæ on a line where the teeth will later appear. This dental lamina grows from the surface downward into the underlying mesenchyme. Concurrently with the development of the dental lamina, at ten places in the mandibular arch and at ten places in the maxillary arch some cells of the dental lamina multiply at a rate faster than the surrounding cells, and ten little knobs of epithelial cells are formed on the dental lamina in each jaw. These little knobs of epithelial cells grow deeper into the underlying mesenchyme (Fig. 78). Each of these knob-shaped structures is the beginning of the information of part of the tooth bud of a primary tooth.

The development of each individual tooth starts with the formation of a *tooth bud*. Now a tooth bud is derived from two embryonic tissues: the part which develops from the dental lamina is derived from ectoderm, and the remaining parts are derived from the mesenchyme which underlies this ectoderm.

A tooth bud is made up of three parts: (1) an *enamel organ*,* which develops from the knob-like growth on the dental lamina (which is, of course, derived from ectoderm); (2) a *dental papilla*, which develops from the underlying mesenchyme (the early connective tissue); and (3) a *dental*

---

*Mesenchyme is an embryonic connective tissue derived from mesoderm.
†Another name for *enamel organ* is *dental organ*.

sac, which also develops from the underlying mesenchyme (Fig. 80). The tissues of the tooth bud produce the tissues of the tooth: the enamel organ produces the tooth enamel; the dental papilla produces the dentin and the pulp; the dental sac produces the periodontal ligament; and the periodontal ligament produces the cementum and the alveolar bone.

The enamel organ is the first part of the tooth bud to form. It develops from the dental lamina as a growth of oral epithelium into the underlying connective tissue (Fig. 78). As it enlarges, the enamel organ acquires the shape of a cap (Fig. 79). The connective tissue which is inside the cap

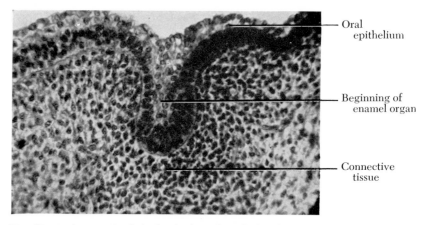

Oral
epithelium

Beginning of
enamel organ

Connective
tissue

FIGURE 78.—Photomicrograph of the beginning of tooth development as seen in a section from a fetal pig. The oral epithelium appears to be growing into the underlying mesenchyme. This is similar to human tooth development. (As seen under high power magnification.)

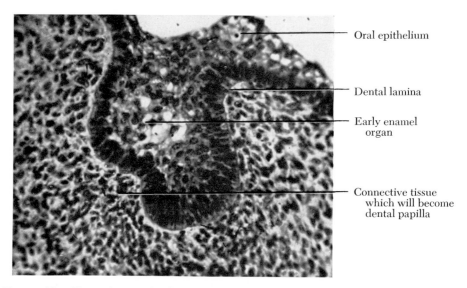

Oral epithelium

Dental lamina

Early enamel
organ

Connective tissue
which will become
dental papilla

FIGURE 79.—Photomicrograph of an early cap-shaped enamel organ in a section from a fetal pig. The dental papilla is becoming discernable. This is slightly more advanced development than that in Figure 78. (As seen under high power magnification.)

undergoes a change and becomes the dental papilla. The connective tissue which is beneath the dental papilla becomes fibrous, the fibers encircling the papilla and part of the enamel organ. These encircling fibers are the dental sac (Fig. 80). The enamel organ for a time remains connected with the oral epithelium by the dental lamina (Figs. 78, 79, 80).

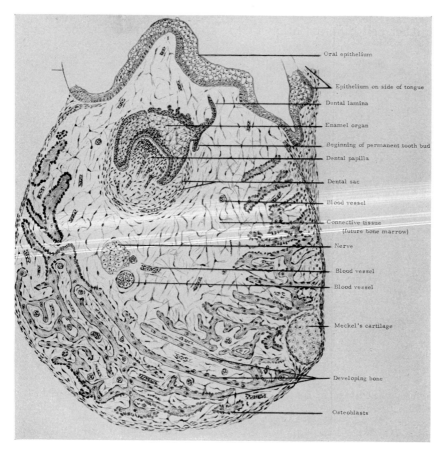

FIGURE 80.—Diagrammatic drawing of a faciolingual section through a developing mandible and tooth bud of a fetal calf. (As seen under low power magnification.)

THE TOOTH BUD

As the tooth bud grows, the cap-shaped enamel organ changes form and becomes somewhat bell-shaped, and four layers are distinguishable (Figs. 80, 81, 82):

The *outer enamel epithelium* is the outside layer of the enamel organ, and is composed of low cuboidal cells.

The *stellate reticulum* is the layer immediately inside the outer enamel epithelium and is composed of a very loose network of epithelial cells.

The *stratum intermedium* is a layer of closely packed, flat epithelial cells cells inside the stellate reticulum.

The *inner enamel epithelium* lines the inside of the bell-shaped enamel organ. It is a single layer of cuboidal cells. This layer of cells is separated from the dental papilla by a basement membrane.

The growing tooth bud changes form rapidly at first, but by the time the four layers of the enamel organ are well defined the shape of the basement membrane has become fixed. When the final shape of the basement membrane is established it marks the line which will become the dentinoenamel junction of the finished tooth.

Further cell differentiation in the tooth bud occurs along either side of the basement membrane. First the cuboidal cells which make up the

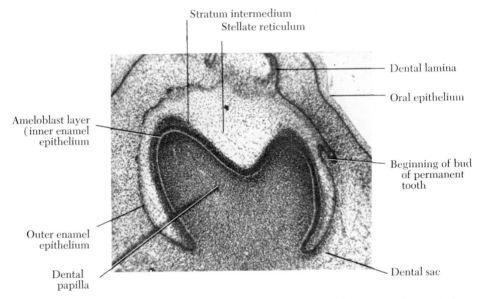

FIGURE 81.—A photomicrograph of the tooth bud of a mandibular posterior tooth from a fetal pig. The enamel and dentin have not yet started to form, but the shape of the dentinoenamel junction can be seen from the configuration of the dental papilla. On the lingual side of this primary tooth bud the bud of the permanent tooth which will succeed it has already started to form. (As seen under low power magnification.)

inner enamel epithelium elongate into columnar cells called *ameloblasts* (Figs. 80, 81 and 82). Formation of the ameloblasts is followed by a change in the peripheral cells of the dental papilla which also take on a columnar form and become odontoblasts (Fig. 82). The ameloblast and odontoblast layers are separated from each other by the basement membrane.

In embryonic development many things are occurring, of course, at the same time. As the early tooth buds are developing they become surrounded by islands of bone which eventually coalesce and form the mandible (or maxillae). Figure 80 is a drawing of a faciolingual section of a forming calf mandible cut through the center of a primary tooth bud. Blood vessels, nerves, and the tooth bud, having formed earlier, are becoming enclosed in the bone of the mandible which is developing around them.

By the time a primary tooth bud has reached the stage of development where ameloblasts and odontoblasts are becoming differentiated, other changes are taking place. Lingual to the enamel organ of the primary tooth bud the dental lamina is giving rise to the beginning of the enamel organ of the succeeding permanent tooth bud (Figs. 80 and 81). The permanent tooth bud will develop slowly as the primary tooth develops and goes into function. Also there occurs disintegration of the dental lamina connecting both enamel organs with the oral epithelium. The cells of the dental lamina break apart into small groups and either gradually disappear or remain as small groups of epithelial cells.

When ameloblasts and odontoblasts have differentiated along either side of the basement membrane in the tooth bud, formation of the hard tooth tissues begins. The earliest formation of the hard tooth tissues in the human embryo occurs during the fifth month in the primary incisors. Dentin formation starts just a little before enamel formation begins.

DENTIN FORMATION

Dentin is composed of (1) a *fibrillar matrix* which calcifies, and (2) *dentinal fibers* which remain uncalcified.

Dentin is formed by the dental papilla. Recent and current studies on dentin are raising questions about details of dentin formation. Until the answers to some of these questions become known, we will present the process as it has long been accepted, recognizing at the same time that here as elsewhere our understanding may be altered as it is increased.

Cytoplasmic processes of the odontobasts form the dentinal fibers; Korff's fibers form the fibrils of the dentin matrix; and cells of the dental papilla produce the cementing substance which surrounds the fibrils of

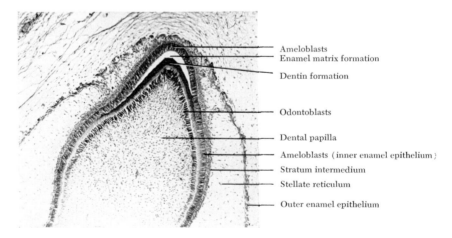

FIGURE 82.—A photomicrograph of the tooth bud of a mandibular anterior tooth of a fetal pig. A small amount of enamel matrix is seen at the tip of the incisal edge. Beneath the enamel matrix, and extending farther cervically, is a layer of dentin. These tissues will become thicker and will be extended cervically. Notice the columnar ameloblast cells and the columnar odontoblasts. The tissue of the dental papilla here has very much the same appearance as does the pulp tissue of a young, fully formed tooth.

the matrix. The first dentin is formed at the incisal edge or cusp tip of a tooth, and formation progresses in a rootward direction. It may be accomplished somewhat in this manner:

The odontobasts, which have differentiated from the fibroblasts of the dental papilla, form a single layer of columnar cells at the line of the dentinoenamel junction (Fig. 82). They start moving inward—that is, they back up toward the center of the pulp. As the cells pull back, they behave as if several spots of their cytoplasm were attached to the basement membrane, causing the cytoplasm to stretch out into several narrow

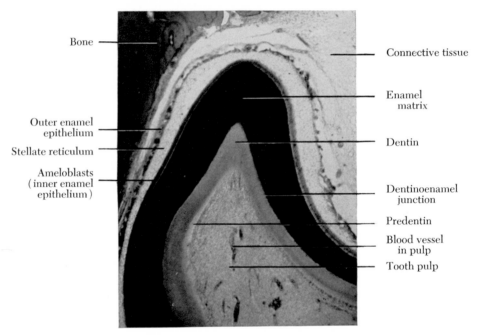

Bone

Outer enamel epithelium

Stellate reticulum

Ameloblasts (inner enamel epithelium)

Connective tissue

Enamel matrix

Dentin

Dentinoenamel junction

Predentin

Blood vessel in pulp

Tooth pulp

FIGURE 83.—A photomicrograph of one cusp of a developing molar tooth of a monkey. The thickness of the enamel matrix appears to be nearly completed. The outer enamel epithelium and the stellate reticulum of the enamel organ are clearly seen; the ameloblast layer is still distinct. In this section the stratum intermedium is not easily distinguishable. The narrow, pale part of the dentin next to the pulp is less calcified than the outer part and is called *predentin*. Notice the bone near the cusp tip. This bone is being resorbed, and its disappearance will permit the tooth to move occlusally.

extensions (Fig. 84). As the pulpward migration of the body of the odontoblasts progresses, the several cytoplasmic extensions of each cell join to make a single dentinal fiber. The part of the odontoblasts containing the nucleus comes to lie some distance pulpward of the basement membrane (now the dentinoenamel junction), but the cells remain connected with the dentinoenamel junction by the cytoplasmic extensions which are branched at their peripheral ends.

Now when the odontoblasts differentiated along the periphery of the dental papilla, there were formed among them heavy corkscrew-shaped fibers called *Korff's fibers*. These were produced by the aggregation of numerous fine fibrils in the dental papilla (see Chapter 5). When dentin formation begins with the odontoblasts moving inward, Korff's fibers remain in place (Fig. 85). With the bulky part of the odontoblast cells out of the way the thick Korff's fibers spread out, somewhat in the manner of a piece of rope becoming unwound and frayed. In this way Korff's fibers separate into tiny fibrils which surround the cytoplasmic extension of the odontoblasts. These are the *fibrils* of the dentin matrix.

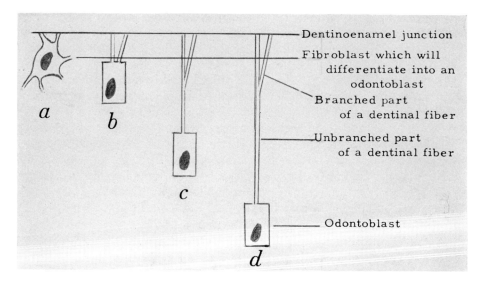

FIGURE 84.—Schematic diagram of the possible manner of formation of a dentinal fiber. (*a*) A pulp cell called a fibroblast will differentiate into a columnar odontoblast. (*b*) The odontoblast has moved away from the dentinoenamel junction, but part of its cytoplasm remains stretched behind in two places. (*c*) The odontoblast has moved farther inward, and its cytoplasmic processes have united. (*d*) The odontoblast has moved still farther inward, and a long dentinal fiber has been formed.

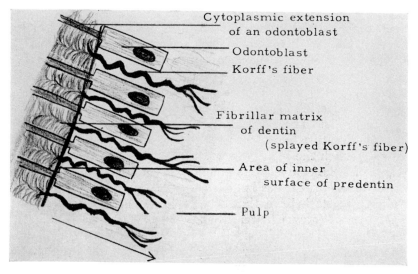

FIGURE 85.—Schematic diagram of odontoblasts and Korff's fibers. Very much enlarged.

9

They are surrounded by an amorphous substance called the *ground substance of the dentin matrix*, which is produced by other pulp cells. The cytoplasmic extensions of the odontoblasts are the *dentinal fibers*. Since the dentin matrix is formed and calcifies around the dentinal fibers, the dentin is perforated by *dentinal tubules* which are, of course, filled with the dentinal fibers.

Dentin matrix calcifies progressively as it is formed. The innermost layer of dentin matrix (next to the pulp) is the most recently formed, and in developing teeth it is not calcified until a successive layer has been formed. This newest, noncalcified dentin is called *predentin* or *dentinoid* (Fig. 83).

Dentin may be produced along the pulpal wall in a tooth of any age as long as the pulp is intact. Dentin formed in older teeth in response to attrition or caries is called *secondary dentin*. The tubules in secondary dentin are fewer and less regular in arrangement than those of the earlier dentin because, due to age changes in the pulps of older teeth, there are fewer odontoblasts, and so fewer dentinal fibers (Figs. 16, 18, 19, and 40).

When dentin formation begins, the forming organ is called the *dental papilla*. After some amount of dentin has been produced the name of the dental papilla is changed and it is called the *dental pulp*.

ENAMEL FORMATION

Tooth enamel is a product of the enamel organ. The ameloblasts produce an organic enamel matrix in which calcium salts later crystalize out of solution making enamel a hard tissue.

Enamel matrix formation starts soon after the beginning of dentin formation. Enamel matrix formation begins at the tips of the cusps (or incisal edge) and progresses cervically, closely following the progress of dentin formation. As the odontoblasts of the pulp move inward leaving dentinal fibers and dentin matrix in the area they once occupied, the opposing ameloblasts move outward, leaving enamel matrix in their wake (Figs. 82 and 83).

Enamel matrix is laid down in the form of enamel rods and interrod substance. The organic matrix of each rod is a product of a single ameloblast. As each ameloblast moves away from the dentinoenamel junction it deposits drops of material. These drops remain lined up behind the ameloblast in such a way that they resemble a string of flattened beads in close union (Figs. 22, 27, 38). They are segments, or units, of the matrix of the enamel rods. This segmentation is visible as cross striations in the enamel rods of mature teeth when such teeth are ground into thin sections and examined with the high power of the microscope. The interrod substance between the enamel rods is believed to be a product of the intercellular substance which lies between the ameloblasts.

Some histologists believe that when the ameloblasts have completed the production of enamel matrix they produce a smooth coating over its surface. This coating calcifies. It covers the entire surface of the tooth crown and is called the *primary enamel cuticle*. This coating is not visible in ground sections of tooth enamel, and so it is not shown in any of the illustrations in this book.

After the enamel matrix is formed to its full width it hardens. This is in contrast to dentin calcification where hardening occurs progressively as succeeding layers of dentin matrix are produced.

The destiny of the enamel organ of the tooth bud is important. As the enamel matrix is being produced and the ameloblasts are moving away from the dentinoenamel junction, the stellate reticulum of the enamel organ narrows and ultimately disappears, and the enamel organ is reduced to a layer of ameloblasts plus a few layers of squamous epithelial cells which are the remains of the rest of the enamel organ. When the ameloblasts have completed the formation of the enamel rods, they change to flattened epithelial cells and blend indistinguishably with the remaining cells of the enamel organ. Thus the enamel organ, originally composed of ameloblasts, stratum intermedium, stellate reticulum, and outer enamel epithelium, has been reduced to a few layers of flattened cells covering the newly formed tooth crown. These combined layers of cells are called the *reduced enamel epithelium* (Fig. 74B).

The reduced enamel epithelium now produces a noncalcified enamel cuticle over the surface of the tooth crown. This is called the *secondary enamel cuticle*. This noncalcified cuticle may remain on the surface of the tooth after the tooth emerges into the oral cavity. There is some disagreement among histologists about the structure of the enamel cuticles.

The reduced enamel epithelium surrounds the crown of the tooth until it emerges into the oral cavity. After the tooth tip emerges, the part of the reduced enamel epithelium which remains surrounding the crown is henceforth referred to as the *epithelium of the gingival sulcus* and the *epithelial attachment* (Figs. 73, 74B-C, 75). The epithelial attachment of a newly erupted tooth is what remains of the original enamel organ of the tooth bud.

ROOT FORMATION

Formation of the dentin and of the enamel begins in the incisal or cuspal areas of the tooth and progresses cervically. Enamel formation stops at the termination of the enamel organ, which is the cervical border of the tooth crown. Dentin formation continues beyond this point, and the dentin of the root is formed (Figs. 74A, E). As the root dentin starts to form, the already formed tooth crown moves occlusally, although the tooth does not emerge into the oral cavity until a considerable portion of the root has been produced. If the tooth has but a single root, the dentin wall forms enclosing a single pulp canal (Fig. 74). If the tooth is to be a multi-rooted tooth, the division of the pulp cavity into two pulp canals, each surrounded by a wall of dentin, is apparent soon after the completion of the crown. Figure 86 is a photograph of a mandibular third molar from which the buccal wall is removed. The crown of this tooth is complete. Dentin has formed beyond the cervical border of the enamel, and a short root trunk is present. In the center of the lower edge of this young tooth pulp there is evidence of its division into two branches, one for the mesial root and one for the distal root. Figure 87 is a similar tooth the roots of which are slightly more advanced in development. Here the

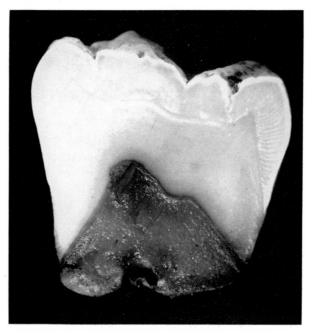

FIGURE 86.—Mandibular left 3rd molar. Buccal side removed. The crown of this tooth is completed; the root has started to form. The lower border of the pulp chamber shows the beginning of a division into two root canals.

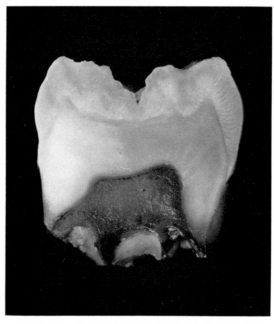

FIGURE 87.—Mandibular right 3rd molar. Buccal side removed. The crown is completed. There is clearly the beginning of development of two roots.

root bifurcation is obvious. Due to drying out of the specimen during preparation, the tooth pulp in each root shows some shrinkage at its lower border, making it erroneously appear, at first glance, that there may be four roots developing.

Figure 88 is a photograph of a mandibular third molar the roots of which have attained perhaps three fourths of their final length. The root canals are broad and their apical openings are large.

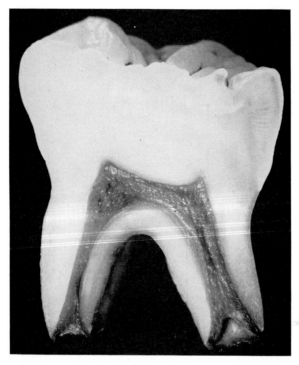

Figure 88.—Mandibular left 3rd molar. Buccal side removed. The roots have attained about three fourths of their length. The root canals are broad, and the openings at the ends of the incompletely formed roots are large.

Figure 89 is a photograph of the buccal surface of a mandibular third molar the roots of which are perhaps about two thirds their final length. The apical openings are very large. In the process of studying extracted teeth students often mistake the short, square shape of such roots as an indication of partial root resorption. A permanent tooth with the apical third of its roots resorbed would have small root canals (because it probably would be an older tooth), and the root ends probably would not have this square shape.

Figure 90 is a tooth similar to the one shown in Figure 89. This picture was taken looking up into the open ends of the root canals. Notice the large size of the root canals and the thinness of the dentin wall.

Root length is not complete until one to four years after the tooth emerges into the oral cavity. A newly emerged tooth has a short root and a very large apical opening. As teeth become older and the root length

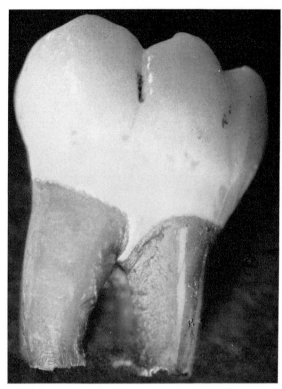

FIGURE 89.—Buccal surface of a left mandibular 3rd molar. The roots have attained about two thirds of their length. The openings at the ends of the incompletely formed roots are large. In this tooth the enamel extends between the roots and meets the enamel on the lingual surface of the tooth.

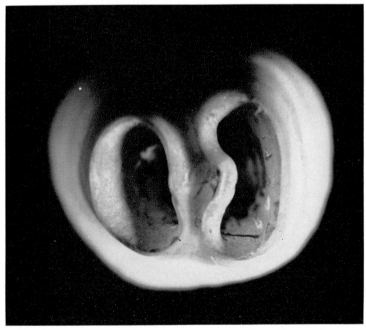

FIGURE 90.—A mandibular 2nd molar. This picture was taken looking into the large openings at the ends of the incompletely formed roots.

is completed, additional dentin continues to form on the pulpal surface of the existing dentin until the root canal becomes narrow and the apical opening becomes small. The stage of development of the root—that is, the size of the root canal and of the apical foramen—is important to the endodontist if accident or dental caries makes endodontic treatment in a child necessary.

FORMATION OF PERIODONTAL LIGAMENT AND CEMENTUM

As dentin is forming apical to the cervical line of the enamel, the circularly arranged fibers of the dental sac become the periodontal ligament around the tooth root. The periodontal ligament produces the cementum which covers the root dentin. It also produces the lamina dura of the tooth socket. As the cementum and the lamina dura are being produced about the forming root, fibers of the periodontal ligament become entrapped in their substance. As the tooth erupts, the periodontal ligament fibers are reoriented. The attachment of the periodontal ligament fibers in the lamina dura and in the cementum holds the tooth securely in the socket (Fig. 53).

As the tooth crown moves occlusally it carries with it the reduced enamel epithelium which covers it. At the cervical border of the reduced enamel epithelium some of its cells seem to pull off in strands which remain stretched like a network in the periodontal ligament around the forming root. This network is called *Hertwig's epithelial sheath*. Later, when the tooth is fully formed and in function, a few fragments of Hertwig's epithelial sheath may still be found upon microscopic examination of the periodontal ligament. These small groups of cells are called the *rests of Malassez*. (See Chapter 7 and Figs. 52, 74 and 76).

ANOMALIES

Development of the teeth may vary in a number of ways from the usual standard. Sometimes less than the normal number of tooth buds develop and an individual has too few teeth (*hypodontia*), or perhaps no teeth (*anodontia*). Sometimes more than the usual number of tooth buds develop and the individual may have a duplication of certain teeth, such as two left maxillary laterals. These extra teeth are called *supernumerary teeth* (super = additional; numerary = number). Sometimes certain teeth have a peculiar shape: the maxillary lateral may be peg-shaped; the maxillary central may be screwdriver-shaped, having a mesiodistal dimension which is smaller in the incisal third than in the cervical portion.

Again, there may be a faulty development of the hard tooth tissues. Enamel development may be so imperfect that the enamel is lost from the surface of the tooth soon after eruption. This condition is hereditary. A more frequent condition is localized enamel hypoplasia (hypo = under; plasia = formation), which is the result of a systemic disturbance during the time the tooth crowns are forming. This is often seen in the form of a pitted line across the facial surfaces of the permanent incisors, the tips of the canines, and the cusps of the first molars in the same mouth. It affects the areas of the teeth that were in the process of formation at the

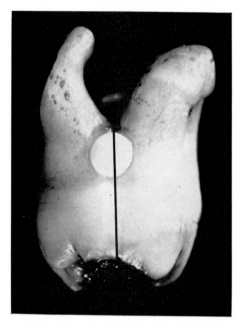

FIGURE 91.—Distal surface of a maxillary right third molar. On the root trunk is an enamel pearl. The tooth was ground to a thin section along the vertical line. See Figure 92.

FIGURE 92.—A ground section of the tooth shown in figure 91. The enamel pearl is in the upper right. The roots are not present here because the section was made at the root furcation. Notice that besides having a formation of enamel in this unusual location, there is a variation in the dentin formation which has resulted in a protursion of dentin beneath the enamel pearl.

time the systemic cause of the hypoplasia occurred. If the systemic cause occurred before the child was ten months old, the maxillary laterals probably will not be affected, because of their normally later development. Still another abnormality is an interference with the calcification of the enamel matrix which produces hypocalcified areas in the enamel. This condition is seen in individuals who have lived during the first eight years

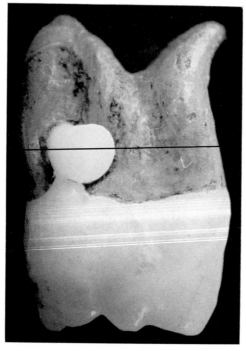

FIGURE 93.—A maxillary right third molar with a very large enamel pearl on the distal surface of the lingual root. The tooth was ground to a thin section along the horizontal line. See Figure 94.

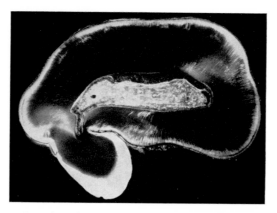

FIGURE 94.—A ground section of the tooth shown in Figure 93. The enamel pearl is in the lower left. In this tooth there is not only a protrusion of the dentin beneath the enamel pearl, but there is also an extrusion of the pulp cavity in the location of the pearl.

10

of their lives in regions where the drinking water contained over 2 parts per million of fluorine. Fluoride in the drinking water causes enamel hypocalcification only when it is consumed during the period of tooth formation; and such hypocalcification is clinically visible only when the fluoride is in amounts in excess of approximately 2 ppm. The hypocalcified areas of enamel soon become stained brown when exposed to the oral cavity, so that there are unsightly brown spots on the teeth. This condition is called *mottled enamel.*

An interesting anomaly which is sometimes seen in the process of examining a collection of extracted teeth is the *enamel pearl*. This is a spot of enamel, usually in the shape of half a sphere, which is found on the roots of teeth. The most frequent location of enamel pearls is said to be on the distal surface of third molars (Figs. 91 and 93), although they are sometimes found on the buccal surface of a molar at the root furcation. Their formation is the result of a small group of cells of Hertwig's epithelial root sheath adhering to the surface of the newly formed root dentin instead of becoming separated from the dentin and moving out into the periodontal ligament. These epithelial cells adhering to the root dentin differentiate into ameloblasts just as the cells of the inner enamel epithelium in the crown area differentiate into ameloblasts, and a drop of enamel (enamel pearl) is then produced on the root.

That the production of an enamel pearl is more than merely a simple matter of the cells of Hertwig's sheath adhering to the root dentin is indicated by the fact that the dentin beneath the enamel pearl in many, if not all, cases protrudes into the pearl. That is, the external dentin surface is not flat, as on the rest of the root: there is a protrusion of dentin which is covered by the enamel pearl (Figs. 92 and 94). In some teeth the configuration of the pulp canal is also altered. In the cross section (Fig. 94) of the tooth shown in Figure 93, there is an extrusion of the wall of the pulp canal beneath the enamel pearl.

Another variation in enamel formation found in molars, chiefly mandibular molars, is an extension of the enamel at its cervical border between the roots of the teeth (Fig. 89). Perhaps this pattern of enamel distribution should not be called an anomaly, as it has been reported to occur in 90 per cent of the mandibular first molars in persons of Mongoloid racial stock. It is unusual in teeth of persons of Caucasian racial stock.

12

Tooth Eruption and the Shedding of the Primary Teeth

TOOTH ERUPTION

Tooth eruption is the combination of bodily movements of the tooth, both before and after the emergence of its crown into the oral cavity, which serves to bring it and maintain it in occlusion with the teeth of the opposing arch. Tooth eruption begins at the time the root starts to form and continues throughout the life of the tooth.

Eruptive Movements

Tooth eruption begins when the crown of the tooth has been formed and the formation of the root dentin starts. In its simplest form tooth eruption may be pictured as the occlusal movement of the tooth brought about, at least in part, by the pressure produced by the lengthening of the root and the development of additional bone beneath the root. Instead of visualizing the process of root formation as one in which the root grows deeper into the jaw, it is necessary to regard the position of the apical end of the developing root as being relatively fixed. As the developing root lengthens, its growing apical end maintains its position and the crown is pushed occlusally. Undoubtedly this concept gives an oversimplified picture of the process, for there is much yet to be learned about tooth eruption.

In the development of the permanent dentition, the movements of tooth eruption vary from little more than this relatively simple process of occlusal movement in the anterior teeth, through a condition of considerable horizontal movement in the premolars, to a highly complex set of rotating and horizontal movements in the molars.

With the exception of the permanent molar teeth the enamel organ of each permanent tooth develops from the dental lamina lingual to its primary predecessor. By the time the primary tooth has emerged into the oral cavity the development of the permanent tooth is well advanced. In the anterior region the permanent teeth continue development lingual to their primary predecessors, but in the region of the premolars a change in relative position occurs. The premolars replace the primary molars. By the time the primary molars have come into occlusion, the crowns of the developing premolars occupy a position not lingual to, but between the roots of the primary molars (Fig. 95). This change in relative positions occurs as a result of a vertical movement of the primary teeth and a horizontal movement of the developing permanent teeth.

The permanent molar teeth do not have predecessors. The enamel organs of the tooth buds of the permanent molars develop from an extension of the dental lamina distal to the position of the primary molars. The first permanent molars develop in approximately the position they will hold upon emergence into the oral cavity. But the crowns of both the second and third molars form in a very different position, and must undergo complicated motions of rotation and forward movement in order to emerge into correct relation to other teeth.

At the time the second and third molars begin to develop neither the maxilla nor the mandible is large enough to accommodate them. The mandibular second and third molars develop in the ramus of the mandible with their occlusal surfaces directed mesially. The second molar usually emerges into the oral cavity in its correct position distal to the first molar. But inadequate jaw development and a failure of sufficient rotating movement in the early stages of eruption sometimes cause the crown of the mandibular third molar to press against the roots of the adjacent second molar. The result of such a positional relationship is an impacted third molar. In Figure 64 is seen a mandibular third molar crown forming in the usual position in the ramus of the mandible.

In the maxilla the second and third molars develop in the maxillary tuberosity with their occlusal surfaces directed distally and buccally. Inadequate jaw development and a failure of sufficient rotating movement in the early stages of eruption may result in the emergence of the maxillary third molar with its occlusal surface directed distally and buccally. The change in position of developing teeth in the jaws is correlated with the growth of the teeth, the growth of the alveolar process, and the growth of the jaws (Fig. 64).

Incidently, in the course of the total process of tooth eruption, the tooth emerges into the oral cavity. Figure 74 is a diagram of some events involved in this emergence. In Figure 74A the tooth crown is nearly complete but root formation has not yet begun. The reduced enamel epithelium covering the crown is separated from the epithelium lining the oral cavity by an area of connective tissue. In Figure 74B root formation is in progress and the crown has moved occlusally. With the occlusal movement of the tooth crown the reduced enamel epithelium has come in contact with the oral epithelium. At the cervical border of the reduced enamel epithelium some cells seem to have broken off and remained as an open network of epithelial cells in the periodontal ligament surrounding the tooth root. This network is *Hertwig's epithelial sheath*. In Figure 74C the epithelial cells which previously covered the incisal edge of the tooth have disappeared and the tip of the tooth has become visible in the mouth. With the emergence of the tooth into the mouth the reduced enamel epithelium becomes known as the *epithelial attachment* (Fig. 74D). This change is merely one of terminology, not a change of cells. With age the cells at the apical end of the epithelial attachment proliferate onto the cementum of the root (Fig. 74E). (Turn to page 117 and re-read the discussion on the epithelial attachment.)

Although the tooth comes into occlusion during the formation of the root, occlusal movement does not cease when the root is completed. Due to continued cementum formation at the root end and to changes in the surrounding bone, occlusal movement may continue, at least intermittently, throughout the life of the tooth. An important need is served by this continued slow eruption. With years of use the occlusal and incisal areas of the teeth are often considerably worn off. The continued occlusal movement of the teeth with advancing years helps to compensate for loss of crown length.

The Mechanism of Tooth Eruption

The mechanism of tooth eruption is a controversial subject. Early occlusal movement seems to be a result of a combination of factors: First, the tissue beneath the growing root probably resists apical movement of the developing root. This results in the occlusal movement of the tooth crown as the root lengthens. Second, bone formation occurs apical to the developing tooth. Other factors, as yet unknown, are probably also involved.

After the root is fully formed further tooth eruption is dependent on changes in the bone surrounding the tooth and additions of cementum to the root apex. Cementum formation continues intermittently throughout the life of the tooth. Bone changes also continue to occur with changes in tooth function.

The mechanism which causes the complex lateral and rotating movements of some of the teeth is a matter which needs additional investigation.

Cervical Exposure Without Occlusal Movement

In young individuals the clinical crowns of the teeth are smaller than the anatomic crowns (Figs. 74C, D, E). As a person ages usually there is an increase in the length of the clinical crown to the extent that some cervical cementum is exposed to the oral cavity. More cementum exposure occurs through the years than can be accounted for by actual occlusal tooth movement. While the teeth undoubtedly do undergo occlusal movement, part of their increased exposure throughout life is due to a progressive loss of soft tissue attachment. This occurs when the apical end of the epithelial attachment, which originally was located at the cementoenamel junction, proliferates (grows) onto the cementum (Fig. 74E) and the coronal end of the attachment, which is the base of the gingival sulcus, likewise moves apically. Eventually cementum is exposed at the cervix of the tooth (Fig. 74G). The apical migration of the epithelial attachment to a limited degree is a normal condition. Exposed cementum is found in the mouths of nearly all individuals who are over forty years old, and in many individuals who are younger.

This apical movement of the gingiva is called *gingival recession*.

Mesial Drift

A number of tooth movements have already been mentioned: (1) the easily recognized occlusal movement of the erupting tooth; (2) the horizontal movement which puts the developing crowns of the permanent premolars between the roots of the primary molars; and (3) the complicated combination of rotating and lateral movements which brings second and third molars into their final position.

In addition to these tooth movements there is a type of tooth movement known as mesial drift. *Mesial drift* is the lateral bodily movement of the teeth on both sides of the mouth toward the midline of the arch. The conditions leading to mesial drift may be understood if we picture the teeth in function. Since teeth are suspended in their sockets by the fibers of the periodontal ligament, they are not rigid in the jaws but undergo considerable movement during the process of mastication. This functional movement produces a rubbing of the contact areas. In newly emerged teeth the contact with adjacent teeth is on a very small area of spherical surface. After years of function the spherical contact areas are worn to flattened surfaces because the teeth have remained in contact. This maintenance of contact is a result of the movement of the teeth toward the midline of the arch—that is, mesial drift.

Mesial drift is possible because of the adaptability of bone tissue. Pressure on the periodontal ligament fibers results in the resorption of the lamina dura, while pull on the fibers results in bone apposition (formation). As the contact areas of the crowns wear, the teeth tend to move mesially, maintaining contact. The slight pressure thus produced on the mesial side of the socket results in slow resorption of the lamina dura. The accompanying tension of the periodontal ligament fibers on the distal side of the root induces apposition of lamina dura bone in this area. As a consequence of these bone changes there is an actual shift in the position of the tooth socket (Fig. 65).

It should be understood that the process of mesial drift is a very slow one, taking place over a period of many years as the mesial and distal contact areas of the tooth crowns wear off.

SHEDDING OF THE PRIMARY TEETH

PRIMARY AND PERMANENT DENTITIONS

The human *primary dentition* is made up of 1 central incisor, 1 lateral incisor, 1 canine, and 2 molar teeth in each quadrant of the mouth. The first teeth to become visible in the oral cavity are usually the primary mandibular central incisors, which emerge when the child is about six months old. The last primary teeth to appear are the maxillary second molars, which appear about the end of the second year. Each tooth of the primary dentition is eventually lost and is replaced by a tooth of the permanent dentition.

The *permanent dentition* consists of 1 central incisor, 1 lateral incisor, 1 canine, 2 premolars, and 3 molars in each quadrant of the mouth. The first permanent tooth to appear is usually a first molar, which emerges just behind the second primary molar when the child is about six years old. The last primary tooth to remain in the mouth is usually the second primary molar. This is replaced by the permanent second premolar in about the twelfth year. The permanent molars have no predecessors. Since the first permanent molars appear in the mouth during the sixth year, when the primary dentition is sometimes still intact, it is important that these teeth be recognized as teeth of the permanent dentition and not be regarded as primary teeth soon to be lost.

In Table 2 will be found the time of emergence into the oral cavity of the teeth of the primary and permanent dentitions, as well as the time of the beginning of hard tissue formation in each of the teeth (See page 145).

THE PROCESS OF SHEDDING

The shedding of primary teeth is the result of the gradual resorption of their roots with the consequent loss of periodontal ligament attach-

Primary canine tooth

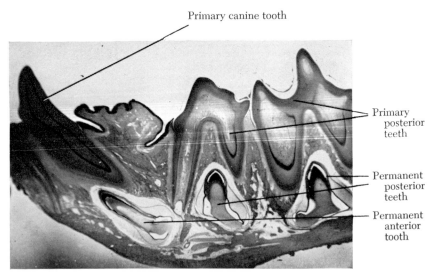

Primary posterior teeth

Permanent posterior teeth

Permanent anterior tooth

FIGURE 95.—A photomicrograph of a longitudinal section of the mandible of a kitten. The primary canine tooth and posterior teeth are in functional position. Beneath the root of the canine tooth and between the roots of the posterior teeth are the developing crowns of the teeth of the permanent dentition. This same kind of arrangement is seen in human teeth. A kitten mandible is used here for illustration because of the difficulty in obtaining suitable human material.

ment. The developing permanent successor, located lingual to, or beneath the root of the functioning primary tooth, creates sufficient pressure by its increase in size to produce resorption of the primary tooth root and of the bone surrounding the root (Figs. 95 and 96). As the root resorbs the tooth loosens. Eventually all periodontal ligament attachment is lost and the rootless crown of the primary tooth literally falls off of the jaw.

An interesting phenomenon frequently observed in children is the alternate loosening and tightening of a primary tooth before it is finally shed. One day the child reports a loose tooth, and several days later the tooth seems to be firmly attached. This reattachment is due to the fact that when resorption of the primary tooth root causes the tooth to become loose, not only is pressure relieved but slight tension seems to be induced on the adjacent connective tissue. This tension stimulates the connective tissue around the resorbed root end to form new cementum on the remaining root end and new bone around the root. This results in the attachment of new periodontal ligament fibers and the tooth tightens in the jaw. But further development of the permanent tooth bud soon causes more resorption of both bone and root. Loosening and reattachment may alternate several times, but as the permanent tooth continues to develop the pressure brought about by its growth will cause sufficient resorption of the primary tooth root to bring about the shedding of the tooth.

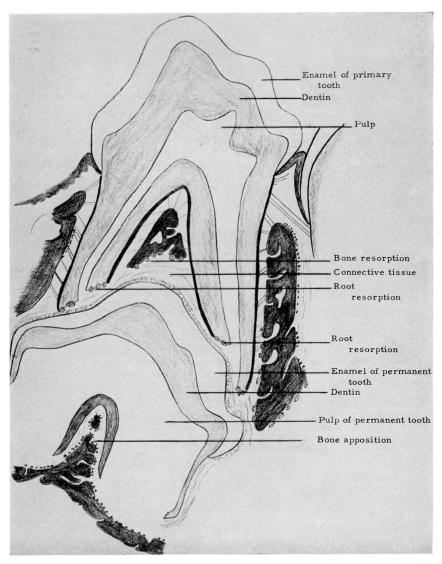

FIGURE 96.—A diagrammatic drawing of a mesiodistal section through a portion of kitten mandible. This drawing was made from the same specimen as the one illustrated in Figure 95, but from a different section. Here there is root resorption on the primary tooth as a result of the growth of the permanent tooth crown. Notice also the resorption of the bone between the roots of the primary tooth. Between the developing roots of the permanent tooth bone growth (bone apposition) is taking place.

Occasionally the relative positions of the primary tooth and its permanent successor are such that the primary tooth root is not subjected to the pressure which would cause its resorption. In this case the permanent tooth may emerge into the oral cavity lingual to the primary tooth which it is supposed to replace. This condition is seen most often in the region of the mandibular incisors.

In cases where the permanent tooth bud has failed to develop, the roots of the primary tooth may resorb even though there is no pressure from a permanent successor; or the primary tooth may retain its roots and continue to function in the mouth for many years.

TABLE 2 - THE CHRONOLOGY OF THE HUMAN DENTITION

		Tooth	Formation of enamel matrix and of dentin begins	Time of emergence into oral cavity
Primary dentition	Maxillary	Central incisor	4 mos. in utero	7 1/2 mos.
		Lateral incisor	4 1/2 mos. in utero	9 mos.
		Canine	5 mos. in utero	18 mos.
		First molar	5 mos. in utero	14 mos.
		Second molar	6 mos. in utero	24 mos.
	Mandibular	Central incisor	4 1/2 mos. in utero	6 mos.
		Lateral incisor	4 1/2 mos. in utero	7 mos.
		Canine	5 mos. in utero	16 mos.
		First molar	5 mos. in utero	12 mos.
		Second molar	6 mos. in utero	20 mos.
Permanent dentition	Maxillary	Central incisor	3 - 4 mos.	7 - 8 yrs.
		Lateral incisor	10 - 12 mos.	8 - 9 yrs.
		Canine	4 - 5 mos.	11 - 12 yrs.
		First premolar	1 1/2 - 1 3/4 yrs.	10 - 11 yrs.
		Second premolar	2 - 2 1/4 yrs.	10 - 12 yrs.
		First molar	At birth	6 - 7 yrs.
		Second molar	2 1/2 - 3 yrs.	12 - 13 yrs.
		Third molar	7 - 9 yrs.	17 - 21 yrs.
	Mandibular	Central incisor	3 - 4 mos.	6 - 7 yrs.
		Lateral incisor	3 - 4 mos.	7 - 8 yrs.
		Canine	4 - 5 mos.	9 - 10 yrs.
		First premolar	1 3/4 - 2 yrs.	10 - 12 yrs.
		Second premolar	2 1/4 - 2 1/2 yrs.	11-12 yrs.
		First molar	At birth	6 - 7 yrs.
		Second molar	2 1/2 - 3 yrs.	11 - 13 yrs.
		Third molar	8 - 10 yrs.	17 - 21 yrs.

Adapted from Orban after Logan and Kronfeld (slightly modified by McCall and Schour)

Index

The **bold face** numerals indicate principal reference in text.

(147)